CAT TRACKS

a novel by

Gordon Aalborg

ISBN: 0-9663397-6-2

Published By:
DELPHI BOOKS
P.O. Box 6435
Lee's Summit, MO 64064
Email: DelphiBks@aol.com
Fax: 816-478-2156

First DELPHI BOOKS printing April 2002
10 9 8 7 6 5 4 3 2 1
A limited edition of this book was published by Hyland House, Melbourne.

Cover design and book layout:
Jim Bisakowski – Desktop Publishing Ltd.

Printed in Canada by Friesens

This novel is a work of fiction. Although it contains references to actual places, these references are used merely to lend the work a realistic setting. All other names, characters and incidents are the product of the author's imagination. Any resemblance to actual persons, living or dead, is entirely coincidental and all events are pure invention.

This novel could only be dedicated to the memory of my grandmother, Bami, my first and probably best teacher about the world of nature, and of my mother.

Thanks: To Rex Anderson of the eagle eye, to Fran Baker, and of course to Deni...for believing.

ONE

The cry began as a fluttering rumble, deep in the cat's throat. As she lifted her striped face to the evening breeze, her voice rose and strained to emerge as a high-pitched, yodeling scream that soared and tumbled with its own echoes through the narrow valley.

Again, and yet again she screamed her imperative wail, until the echoes mingled to sound like a chorus of souls in torment. Then she paused with both large ears perked for an answer. She was perched on a broad, flat rock, well up on the rubble-strewn slope of the gorge, where her instincts told her the breeze would carry her mating call far beyond the boundaries of the territory she had claimed for nearly seven years.

A huge animal, with generations of feral wildness behind her, her skull was broad, as was the thick, solid tail with its faintly marked rings. There was no patch of pure white fur on her muscular body; her coat was a muddled crazy-quilt of stripes and blotches where the tones and half-tones of black and brown and tan and creamy fur took a distinct pattern only on her face and tail. Even sitting completely exposed on open ground, she was virtually invisible. Until she moved.

The first of the cat's more recent ancestors to run wild had been a medium-sized white female abandoned by an itinerant prospector. That had occurred during the early gold-rush days in the Brindabella Ranges, a dagger of rough, rugged high country that stabbed north from the Snowy Mountains to divide the watersheds of the Goodradigbee River from the far larger drainage of the Murrumbidgee. Since that time, the strain of feral cats had been strengthened by periodic infusions from stray farm cats, the cats of various prospectors and bushmen and, in later years, the animals callously abandoned by residents of Canberra, Australia's national capital.

Included had been cats of all colors and breeds, but natural selection had weeded out the bright, easily seen ones, the natural prey of foxes—another introduced predator with devastating effect on native wildlife—the soaring wedge-tailed eagles or the silent night-hunters, the Powerful Owls. Long fur, a recessive genetic trait, had been lost in the mingling of breeds, so the old she-cat's fur was short in length, but solid and dense through exposure to the wet and chilling mountain winters. She was the color of survival, a moving shadow among other shadows as she prowled in a ceaseless hunt for food. A perfect killing machine, strong, powerful, quick and deadly, she was the classic example of her particular breed, a feral beast as truly wild as the great cats of Africa and Asia, having no further link, however tenuous, with domesticity.

Technically, she would be classed as a feral animal—a domestic animal gone wild, reverting to a state of natural wildness. Certainly, in Australia, no cat is a "native" animal, though no one is quite certain just how the first cats got there. With early European settlers? Chinese or Asian sailors? Or, perhaps, even earlier; before any contributor to Australia's recorded history. Freed by accident or design into a land with essentially no enemies and an abundance of food, feral cats are such an integral factor in the Australian bush that no place, however remote, is free of them. And those that have been savage for many generations are as large, as fierce and as truly undomesticated as the European wild-cat, the primeval ancestors of all cats.

As the evening faded through shades of purple into the darkness of the valley night, the she-cat gave one final, demanding scream, but she stayed hardly long enough to appraise the dying breeze for an answer. The cooling air was flowing downward as it had risen with the warming currents of the day, and she sniffed at it restlessly, her long, supple whiskers twitching as she searched the air currents for any message they might carry.

Had there been a tomcat within the sound of her mating cries, she would have known it. Like all cats, she depended more upon her ears and light-sensitive eyes for information than upon her nose, but her sense of smell was fully adequate for her needs.

She stood with both ears fully cocked as the echo of her final scream drifted into silence, then gathered herself to leap smoothly from her perch and lope down through the scrub toward the tumbling waters of the river. Despite her size, she seemed a ghostly presence in the dim light, moving silent as a wraith of smoke.

The point from which she had been calling was downstream from where tiny Condor Creek splashed headlong to join the Cotter from the west, and the old cat moved southward past the junction as she patrolled the valley, traveling steadily upstream toward the narrow concrete ford which humans called Vanity Crossing. The ford and the narrow gravel forest track leading to it were the only evidence of human intrusion into the old cat's domain, and to her the track was the most southerly boundary of her territory. Sometimes she crossed there herself, bounding lightly across from stone to stone on the piles of rock which were occasionally placed to mark the lower boundary of the ford.

This night, however, she didn't travel that far south. The tiny rustle of a scurrying rodent caught her broad ears and she turned aside. Step by step, each one a delicate, silent and invisible movement, she advanced on the sound, until finally she was within range. The epitome of patience, she would spend five minutes, or twenty if it were needed, in the resolute advancement of her stalk. Her heavy body hugged the ground, and each movement was so slow and deliberate that she seemed not to move at all.

Only her tail, hidden from her intended prey by the bulk of her body, seemed alive. Like an independent thing, separate from the camouflaged ghostliness of the cat herself, it moved in a delicate, tight-circling motion as her heightening senses built up the tension. Her striped face blended perfectly with the dry grasses and the scattered fronds of underbrush and shadow, and when she reached her decisive launching site, she was forced to consciously restrain a tiny growl of satisfaction. A last pause—the heavy muscles of her hindquarters bunched beneath her—then one surge of those mighty flanks drove her in a flying, slashing attack. Her mobile front paws smashed down on her prey, holding it pinioned until her flashing ivory fangs could clamp tightly in her favorite death grip, a single, snapping clasp on the neck of her victim. The rodent died without even knowing he had been attacked.

Ripping open the quivering small form with her fangs, the cat first licked at the entrails, using her rough, mobile tongue to remove shreds of flesh. She slashed off chunks of flesh and swallowed them in individual gulps. She ate everything, even the feet and skull. Then she carefully licked at her paws and used them to groom her face before moving on.

She was hungry, a hunger given by the growing mating urge inside her, and before the night ended she killed four small brown rodents, three tiny frogs and one fairly large bush rat. All but the rat died the same way, but with her hunger satisfied, she prolonged the rat's death by tossing it aside and then pouncing on it again and again.

She ate little of the rat, having fed quite adequately from her earlier kills, but the playing was a temporary release for her growing restlessness. Fully in season, the survival demands of her instinct had made her tense, irritable. It had been a full year since she had been mated, because the relative isolation of her territory had provided little incentive for roving tomcats. The last one had been a ragged stray from the Pierce's Creek forestry station to the northeast, and the result was four kittens of identical coloring to herself. Perhaps the tomcat's seed had been weak; two of the kittens died before their weaning. The other two hadn't lasted much longer. A roving dog fox had raided the den while the old cat hunted food, and she had returned to find only memories, and those overshadowed by the rancid scent of fox.

The mating before that had provided only two kittens, and both had fallen prey to the silent talons of a large Powerful Owl. The old cat knew the owl, but due to her tremendous size and ferocity the cat had no fear of him. She had, in fact, no real enemies; the fox who dared confront her would be foolish, and even the extremely rare dingo that wandered down from the Brindabellas to the west was no serious threat.

Her range in the Cotter Valley was a good hunting ground, with plenty of native marsupials, abundant bird life, and a wide range of reptiles, frogs and small lizards. She lived well, but alone.

The territorial instinct is far stronger in the feral cat than in tame house cats. The old female had defended her territory fiercely against any and all other females, including her own grown kittens, and except when her heat cycle demanded the need of a tomcat, she avoided their presence deliberately. She would allow no tomcat to settle within her territory at the best of times, and when she was with kittens she had good reason to fear the males' uneven dispositions.

Next morning, as the sun warmed the rocks and outcroppings along the river, she slowed her pace, then finally abandoned travel entirely to lie sprawled on a warm boulder and let the sunshine lull her into easy slumber. She didn't sleep soundly; her ears constantly twitched and turned to catch the sounds of the bush around her, and her nose sifted and catalogued the myriad scents that were carried on the rising breeze. It was almost noon before she stretched, reaching out with each paw and shivering the heavy muscles of her shoulders and flanks. Then she strode deliberately back into the scrub along the edge of the water, moving slowly, but with total alertness as she neared the man-made track to the ford.

A vagrant breeze brought her to a sudden halt, nostrils twitching at the combined odors of wood-smoke and people. But underlying it all, so faint as to seem almost a memory, was the tantalizing scent of another cat—a male. She had already turned in her tracks, automatically fleeing the smell of man, when she caught the other flavor, and her inner urgings took immediate control.

Her throat quivered as the mating scream poured from it.

TWO

Jack Fielding halted his A.C.T. ranger-service truck in the middle of the ford and stared with angry disgust at the rubbish-strewn sand bank upstream from him. Beer cans, soft-drink cans and empty stubbies were scattered everywhere, along with brightly-colored wrappings and gleaming shards of tinfoil. On the far side of the ford, plumes of smoke proclaimed the presence of visitors, and although it wasn't yet the really dangerous bush-fire season with its stringent fire bans, he could tell from the smoke that this particular fire was far larger than any picnic required. His worries decreased slightly as he chugged through to the other side and saw the rump of Dave Bates' battered utility sticking out of the bush; at least old Dave would ensure that the fire was safely out once the offending picnic group had left.

Parking his own vehicle at the edge of the track, Jack strolled through the sand to where he could get a closer look at the scene, and arrived in time to see the form of a large Siamese tomcat hurtle into the arms of a blue-eyed five or six-year-old girl, almost knocking her over. Beside the fire, a burly man of about thirty-five tried vainly to keep some sausages from falling through a grill into the roaring flames while a huge chunk of T-bone steak burned beyond recognition. Jack sighed, not at all relishing the task before him.

Stepping into the open, he coughed to announce his presence, then said, "Excuse me."

The man didn't look up, although the pretty blonde woman beside him turned toward Jack and the little girl gave him a tentative grin.

"Excuse me," he said again, louder this time, then winced as the man flinched at the sound of his voice and tipped a sausage into the flames. Jack, who stood six-foot-four and had been compared to America's legendary Paul Bunyan, got an incautious, angry curse for an answer as the man turned to stare at him with hostile, angry eyes.

The man turned and looked down at the charring sausage, then his eyes rose again to meet Jack's. "Thanks a lot," he said bitterly. "I really needed that. Now what the hell do you want?"

"I just wondered if you know that you're not supposed to have fires except in proper fireplaces," Jack said easily. He called it his gentle approach, and the one he always started with, even when he knew it wasn't likely to work. Rangers in the Australian Capital Territory were trained to accept public relations as an integral part of their work, not least because they were so often in contact with diplomatic staff from all over the world.

The man at the fire was an Australian, by his voice, and not a happy one. He rose to his feet, scuffling his expensive track shoes in the sand. He looked down at his fire, which had swallowed up the sausage, then back at Jack Fielding. "What's the matter with this fireplace?" he demanded. Then, before Jack could answer, "Besides, I don't see any fireplaces around here.

If I'm supposed to use a proper fireplace, where are they?"

"We don't have any here," Jack said, keeping his voice calm and composed, "because this isn't a place we want to encourage people to build fires."

"Rubbish," was the truculent reply. "Good picnic spot, there should be a fireplace. And for your information, there aren't any fire bans on."

The man's wife said, "I'm sorry...we didn't know." She began pushing sand into the flames, gently, so as not to get it all over the smoldering meat, but her husband stopped her.

"Now look here," he said to Jack. "If you want people to use fireplaces, you have to provide them. You can't just come in here and tell me I'm supposed to stop my barbecue halfway through because of some silly damned regulation."

"It isn't a silly regulation, sir. It's for your own safety as much as anything. There are proper barbecues back at Pierce's Creek, and various others in other locations. There aren't any here because it's been decided this area isn't to be developed yet. And I'm not asking you to put out your fire right this minute, just to be very careful with it."

He turned to go, afraid his own anger would escape if the argument continued. Clearly, this wasn't the moment to begin this family's education about proper use of the forest. But when the man shouted after him, "It's a stupid bloody rule," Jack turned back in a single, abrupt motion.

"I didn't make the rule," he said, "any more than I made the one against letting pets run loose out here. However, I must enforce the rules."

He could have bitten his tongue when he saw the little girl clutch tightly at the big tomcat until it squalled. Jack hadn't meant to say anything, since the regulation was seldom enforced except in nuisance cases, but anger had stripped the caution from his tongue. Most people he had to deal with, however ignorant of proper behavior in the bush, were at least reasonable when approached the right way. This fellow, he decided, would be unreasonable at the best of times.

Jack's feelings were borne out when the man turned his anger on the child, shouting at her to lock the cat in the car as she'd been told. Confused and hurt by her father's outburst, the child stood clutching at her pet, tears forming in her brilliant blue eyes. Her mother moved to ease the tension, but the man moved first. He snatched the cat from the child's arms, and, ignoring its angry attempts at retaliation, slogged through the sand toward his car.

"Don't you hurt Toby," the child cried, running after him. But Royal Blue Tobias of Newcastle II was in little danger of being hurt. The large bluepoint Siamese, probably the finest example of his breed in south-eastern Australia, twisted his boxy face into a fierce yowl, flashed his razor-sharp claws, dug into the man's arm, and clawed himself free before they'd gone ten steps.

Howling with pain, the man scrambled for a fresh grip on the tomcat and received another slash across the knuckles. The cat was as angry as the man, whom he clearly didn't like, and he wasn't about to be picked up again.

He wasn't about to be picked up by anyone else, either. The incensed and frightened cat doubled back behind a large gum tree, circled the now-dying fire, and was cautiously eyeing all the people when the banshee wail of the female cat's mating cry surged down the valley.

Toby halted, bolt upright. His dark ears perked and he raised one forefoot like a dog on point. The bluepoint tail twitched behind him as he stood listening, especially the little crooked bit at the end. The second screaming yowl followed close on the first, and the Siamese moved from rigid stillness to blurring, silent motion as he bolted straight past Jack Fielding's legs and out across the track, where he disappeared into the heavy scrub along the riverbank. In the silence that followed, Jack heard Toby's own, distinctive Siamese voice raised in answer to the summons.

What followed was the tumult of the child's tears, her mother's vain attempts to soothe her, and her father's raging verbal attack on Jack Fielding—as if the cat's escape had been the ranger's fault. Forgotten were the charred snags and ruined steak, even the illegal and dying fire. The man's only interest seemed to be the loss of an expensive, prize-winning show cat that had vanished like smoke into the almost impenetrable scrub along the river.

THREE

The sounds of an argument, rather than the cry of a female cat in heat, yanked old Dave Bates out of his peaceful nap. Leaving the shade of his truck, shaking his head at the disturbance, he rose to his feet. Then, finger-combing his still-thick silver hair, he strolled through the scrub.

He arrived in time to see an entire family—father, mother and child—surge forth to hunt for a missing, elusive tomcat; a costly show-cat named Royal Blue Tobias of Newcastle II.

Toby, however, was answering a far stronger, more alluring, and more demanding call than even a distraught child could provide. His instincts, for the moment, left him blind to his association with humans, deaf to the cries of his owners. While the family searched the jungle of scrub near the crossing for a glimpse of his soft tan coat, Toby was half a mile downstream, seeking a place to cross the twinkling waters so that he could join the huge feral she-cat.

"He'll likely come back in a day or two, once his business is done," old Dave told his friend Jack Fielding, as they stared at the water and listened to the cries of the family. "That's if he comes back at all."

"If he comes back at all," Jack echoed. The fringe areas of the Australian Capital Territory—areas near habitation, areas that favored picnic and recreation sites—had large populations of feral cats, enough that trapping and disposing of them was classed as an ongoing program. This far out, however, there were no traps and less likelihood of anybody catching up with the romantic tomcat...unless he returned to the picnic site of his own volition.

The two men discussed the problem of feral cats and their devastating destruction of native Australian wildlife until the family abandoned their search. Then the only course of action was to record a name and address, and promise to capture the cat should it return. There was little else Jack and Dave could do, despite the empathy both men felt for the little girl.

"I hope he does come back, for the kiddie's sake," said Dave, fingering his salt-and-pepper beard as he strolled back to his truck. "But the man's a fool for bringing the tom out here in the first place. I'm a bit surprised, too, considering the value of the beast."

"Personally, I can't imagine paying a fortune for any cat," Jack said. "And if I did, I sure wouldn't be bringing it on picnics with me. You know, don't you, that there's not much chance we'll find it again?"

"Yes, I know, but you wouldn't want to tell them that. Especially not the child. And we could get lucky. I'll be camping down here for a day or two. The fishing isn't bad and I've nothing else to do. So I'll keep an eye open, and maybe if there's somebody here the tom will come back. You can't ever tell. I'd imagine he's never learned to hunt, and the old queen won't feed him for long. Unless he's awful stupid he'll come back to where he remembers people and tucker."

"Thanks, mate, I'd appreciate it. If it weren't for the kiddie, I wouldn't care a bit. The cat's probably better off out there than anywhere near that bloke...the kiddie's dad. And I think the cat knows it. They didn't like each other, you could tell."

The two friends parted, both aware that should Toby survive, he could join countless other cats running wild, brutally abandoned by owners too lazy to keep them. Pet abandonment was a continuing problem at the more popular campsites and picnic areas in the Australian Capital Territory.

FOUR

The female cat was growing desperate. Poised on the eastern bank of the river, she mewed and coaxed and pleaded in muted tones, but to no avail. The Siamese tomcat was terrified at the thought of entering the water. They were nearly three quarters of a mile downstream from the crossing, kept apart by the deep, surging channel with its wide, sunken pools at either end. Toby was adding his own Siamese yowls as he tried to convince the she-cat to get herself over to join him. His voice had that special abrasiveness of all Siamese cats, but the message sounded clear enough. He grew even more insistent as they paced farther north, moving to where the river narrowed and then sprawled into shallows just before its junction with little Condor Creek.

There, it was possible for either cat to cross, although not without getting wet. There, the water lost its force, spreading wide across the shallows of a gravel bar, then spilling into a new channel and a dark, deep hole at the junction. For Toby, terrified by the sight of more water than he had ever seen in his life, there was an added problem. He had the broadness of the river before him, and the narrower but still fearful channel of the creek on his left flank.

He wanted to join the female whose tantalizing odor wafted across to him, but his fear of the water was stronger. The female, though not averse to getting wet, simply didn't want to be on the same side of the river as the people she could hear calling and crashing through the brush.

As she watched, Toby moved to the edge of the gravel, poking at the water in tentative gestures with one slender forefoot. Each time, he withdrew in fearful haste, shaking his foot with disgust at the chill moisture. The female continued her plaintive pleadings, but he could not shake off his fears. She turned and ran further downstream, but he was stalled by the narrow, noisy flow of the creek, and couldn't follow. Finally, with a gesture that would have indicated exasperation in a human, she shook her huge head angrily and plunged swiftly across the shallows. Her flying lunges sprayed water in droplets that glistened briefly in the sunlight before rejoining the river.

Toby was ecstatic. As she reached his side and shook the water from her thick coat in a series of convulsive, shuddering gestures, he pranced around her and voiced his satisfaction in typical Siamese fashion. Then they both stood still, staring cautiously as they observed the formalities of touching noses and smelling at each others' scent glands.

The human voices, for an instant, were forgotten, but only for an instant. Then Toby's name was called again, seemingly closer this time, and the huge female's reaction revealed her fear. Shifting against the tomcat, she forced him toward the water, and when he balked, she moved into it ahead of him, again using her voice and movements, goading him to follow. It was enough; Toby would never have crossed the water to her, but beside her was a different story. He didn't like it, and his voice recorded his protest, but he went.

Once across, the female took immediate command, as if sensing the tomcat's inexperience and his inexplicable lack of fear at the strange loud noises in the scrub across from them. Turning after only a brief exchange of sniffing explorations, she bounded away . through the underbrush, heading downriver and into the roughness of the steep gorge that lay below the junction of river and creek. Toby followed meekly, unsure of the terrain. A large, well-cared-for animal in the peak of show condition, he didn't have the sheer physical strength or the wild-nurtured resilience and power of the older, larger cat. His muscles by comparison were soft and flabby, his feet tender.

When he began to fall behind, footsore and wearied by their trek through the jungles of blackberry thicket and heavy, interlaced ti-tree scrub, the she-cat paused only long enough to let him catch up. Then, after a minimum of cajoling, she would leap ahead again, moving them farther and farther from the crossing.

Finally, they migrated into the high, dry reaches of the gorge that dropped with startling sheerness in a welter of broken rock, rubble and scrubby river oak and brush to reach the river. Here, the female felt safe from the far-distant interruption of human noise.

Toby was nearing exhaustion, but his own mating instinct was aroused, and seemed to provide new reserves of strength. In a tiny area where alluvial soil had allowed the growth of strong, low grasses, he and the female stopped their flight and rested.

At long last, there was time for intricate examinations, the nose-touchings and sniffings that established each cat's full identity to the other, along with their growing sexual requirements. Toby began to display a dominance that was his own part in the mating rituals, but he was a young cat, and had never been put to stud, so he moved with a reticence and unsureness that slowed the displays. The she-cat began everything, throwing herself into the grass, rolling and then writhing about with tiny, mewing whines. She threw herself against Toby, crouching and rubbing against his shoulders and legs, swatting at him with her forepaws and rocking her head up and down, back and sideways, in the female submissiveness that also was part of the ritual.

Toby followed, his tiredness forgotten and his body vibrant with the growing insistence that his instincts provided.

The she-cat batted her forepaws at him, her claws carefully retracted, then turned and ran in small circles as he tried to mount her. Whenever he showed signs of flagging interest, she turned again on him with movements instinctively calculated to make him respond. And finally, when the rituals demanded it, she allowed him to force her down, his teeth locked at the nape of her neck as he mounted her.

When it was over, she turned and batted her paws at him again, but this time with claws extended, and he retreated in confusion as she snarled and hissed at him. But only for a moment. Then, she rolled about on her back before sitting up quietly and beginning her toilet.

Very soon, she was eager again, and she began to tease and excite the tomcat, readying him to resume his role as the aggressor. They mated several times through the twilight and into the fullness of the night, at intervals interspersed with playfulness and rest.

The approach of dawn brought Toby groggily to his feet, his stomach complaining bitterly and his limbs aching from the unaccustomed travel. He found the female awake, anxious to be on the hunt, and he followed her meekly as she led him away through the scrub.

His inexperience cost them their first meal, a pair of marsupial mice feeding quietly near a hollow log. Toby couldn't resist a moan of anticipation, and the mice disappeared in a scurrying rustle of dry leaves and litter as they sought safety before either cat could pounce. The female growled her disapproval, and when they sighted the next potential meal, Toby was quiet.

It was a large brown bush rat, and it shambled across the forest floor with blithe unconcern for the vague, striped shadow that moved with it. The stalk was quick and the female's deadly pounce and snapping fangs dispatched the rat with only a single, futile squeal.

The female's instincts took over then, and for an instant the cats' relationship hung in the balance. She was totally survival oriented; sharing had no place in her instincts. But Toby, after her spitting, snarling reaction to his approach, wisely hung back until she had eaten her fill. Even then, he ate cautiously, aware of the she-cat's suspicion and throttled anger.

The entire business of hunting and killing and sharing the kill was difficult for both animals. To the female, throughout her life a lone hunter, it was alien to even conceive of sharing her kill with any but her own kittens. She had none of the friendly pairing that often occurs among house cats, and it was only because her sexual stirring made her restless and not overly hungry that she allowed Toby to share. As for Toby, whose friendly nature made it natural for him to rush in expecting his share, his instincts provided protection. They made him aware of the female's edginess, forced him to hang back until she would grudgingly allow him to feed on the rank, hot meat so different from what he was used to.

When the female killed the second time, a small bearded dragon lizard, she ate only sparingly before moving aside with barely-muted hostility to allow Toby a share. Her third kill, a tiny spotted frog, she ate herself, growling her warning to the Siamese when he approached.

They lazed through the warmth of the following day, sprawled on the sunny rocks and idly playing the exercise games cats will play. Toby caught a fat, sluggish butterfly and several grasshoppers, but only toyed with them, not recognizing them as food. He and the she-cat mated twice during the day, and with the sighing breezes of evening, began to move into the hunting routine again.

This time, the female led the way back upstream, not consciously drifting toward the edge of her territory again. Her mating need was almost sated and had diminished.

That night she changed her hunting technique, moving into the trees to feast on roosting birds and a small sugar glider she stalked with fierce determination. Toby managed to capture one lone marsupial mouse and a bird that fluttered helplessly to the ground after the female's assault on the roost. The two cats dined separately, though near each other.

As dawn approached, the female's need of Toby had waned to the point where she had begun to find him—and his presence on her territory—increasingly offensive. Despite his absence from human contact during the recent past, the taint of human odor hung on him, and that, too, bothered the huge feral cat. She began to respond to his advances with growing hostility, which annoyed Toby, and his innate masculine dominance made him try to counter her hostility with growing physical dominance.

Finally, he pushed too hard. As he attempted to force her into still another mating, she turned on him with flashing claws and ferocious spitting hisses. Her ears were laid back and she crouched, not in the mating position, but in an attitude of hostile defense. As Toby lashed out at her in half-hearted anger, her defensive attitude changed to one of aggressive rage, and she erupted in a blur of slashing forefeet that chopped deep gouges in Toby's muzzle. Anger made him squall with rage and swipe back at her, but he was no match for her rugged strength. She attacked boldly and within a minute had put him to rout with deep claw wounds on his face, neck and shoulders.

Screaming in pain, he spun around and ran, but not before the raging she-cat had laid gashes down the flank he exposed. She followed him only briefly, snarling and hissing her anger, then turned and trotted cockily back downstream. His part in her life had been played, and her instincts allowed no sentiment, no requirement for his further companionship. When her kittens were born some two months in the future, the presence of Toby or any other male cat would only be a danger to them.

Toby ran almost blindly for several hundred yards, not aware of where he was, or which direction he should be seeking. Purely by chance, he emerged at the bottom of the hill where the gravel track to the ford began to level out, and he turned down the grade, following the course of least resistance. He was still vaguely confused by the she-cat's change in attitude, and he hurt. Her claws had raked deep gouges in his hide, and his injuries combined with his tiredness and sore feet to make him lurch drunkenly down the side of the road until he reached the wide-flowing waters of the ford at Vanity Crossing.

Across the river, a thin tendril of smoke rose from a tiny fire, and Toby smelled the familiar odor of frying bacon...and of man. He could see the haunch of a vehicle protruding from the trees, but not the fire or the man beside it. And before him, the wide, smooth water, with no suggestion of a crossing place fit for a cat.

On his left, the broken rock loomed in a high wall that forced the curve in the river above the ford. To the right, the brisk flow below the ford churned white and angry.

There was no choice; for Toby it was a slow and difficult trek as he wended his way back and around the crown of looming rock. Ultimately, he reached a point directly across the creek from where a human sat silently beside the fire, and Toby stared down, his blue eyes narrowed into slits.

Opening his mouth, he yowled his hurt and his displeasure at the frothing water as it spilled around a curve and into a deep, black pool below his perch.

Nothing happened, so Toby yowled again, even louder, and yet again. His dark-tipped tail lashed back and forth, and he canted from one forefoot to the other, his ears flicking with anticipation.

The smell of cooking food caused his stomach to create strange noises, and the saliva from his mouth made him lick at his muzzle and shake his head with frustration. He yowled again, as loud as he could throw out the raucous, distinctive squall of a Siamese cat. And this time old

Dave Bates heard him.

Startled, the old man looked up, and shook his head as he noted the cat's bloody and disheveled appearance. He called softly to Toby, then rose and began walking back toward the ford, moving slowly and keeping an eye on Toby as the cat moved parallel with him on the other bank.

Toby, frantic with pleasure, bounded stiffly on both front paws and treated his rescuer to a chorus of growls and yowls and mews of undisguised pleasure.

Dave waded across the ford to receive a joyous bundle of Siamese cat as Toby leaped into his outstretched arms and snuggled there, secure at last. Immediately, he began to purr.

Toby was so pleased at being back in human company, with the prospects of a decent meal in the immediate future, that he didn't even protest when Dave paused in mid-stream to gently sponge the blood from the cat's injuries.

"Whoooeee," the old man whistled softly as he saw the great gouges in the once-flawless coat. "No more cat shows for you, old son. And I'll bet you won't be the most popular cat in the world when I get you home, either, except with your little girl."

Toby voiced his own opinion in a chorus of purring growls, and when they reached the far bank he resisted the old man's attempt to put him down. Not until they reached the fireside and its strong odor of frying bacon did the cat allow himself to be freed, whereupon he immediately stalked over, stood near the pan, and waited noisily for his breakfast.

After Dave had cleaned up the campsite and safely extinguished the fire, Toby allowed himself to be carried into the cab of the truck. He curled up against the old man's leg and slept as the ancient utility ground its way into the sprawling suburbs of Canberra.

There, he was greeted with suitable ceremony and tears of relief, especially from the little girl who loved him so. The only difficult part of it all, for Toby, was the trip to the veterinarian, who cleansed his wounds, then checked him for fleas and assorted other vermin.

If Toby had any thoughts at all for the she-cat with whom he'd mated, they were made lackluster by the comforts of gourmet cat food and a plush cushion embroidered:

ROYAL BLUE TOBIAS OF NEWCASTLE II

FIVE

The kittens were born into darkness during a two-hour period in the middle of a dark and rainy night. Being blind and deaf as they emerged in their shiny sacks of membrane, they could not notice the darkness. As the she-cat deftly nipped away the membrane and chewed through the umbilical cord of each arrival, their only senses were of smell and instinct. Tiny bodies, still slick from the birthing and the female's rough, invigorating tongue, clawed and squirmed and struggled their way to her teats, where they clamped upon her with tiny mouths and kneaded at her with their forepaws.

The first three, the females, came easily and

quickly, with barely enough time between them for the mother to lick them dry and start them on their vital journey to her milk. All three were suckling lustily when the fourth and final kitten arrived.

The last was a male, slightly smaller than his three sisters and with unmistakable signs of his Siamese parentage. The females would show it in their builds, eventually, but the tiny male already had the definitive Siamese color points against pale, ghost-gray baby fur. The females exemplified the mottled, tabby coloration of their mother.

They arrived exactly sixty days after the mating, a two-month period in which the old she-cat had become increasingly heavy and sluggish with the weight of the new life within her. For the fortnight prior to the birthing, she had also become restive and secretive about her movements, searching both day and night for food and the proper place, to her mind, for her den.

She rejected several possibilities before choosing the deep cavern high on the slope near the junction of the Cotter with Condor Creek. From many points of view it was the near-perfect den—deep, narrow, warm and dry, with a small secluded nook in the hillside that offered a completely sequestered playground for the kittens once they were old enough to require it. During her prenatal ramblings, the old cat had investigated and rejected other sites, including two she had used in the past.

One old site had been a former wombat burrow, and although it had served the female well enough three years before, the signs that a fox had been using it turned her away with a nose-wrinkling disgust at the rank enemy scent. The other possibility was the den she had used the last time, but she passed it up because of the faint memory of a freak flood and the problems she had faced because of it.

On the move almost constantly in the last days of the pregnancy, she slept in short naps and hunted steadily to provide her swollen body with much needed sustenance. Always staying well away from the den, she slaughtered birds and marsupial mice, lizards and bush rats—anything she could manage to catch and kill.

Because of her decreased speed and agility, she found the hunting difficult and arduous, and she often missed what seemed to be easy prey because she misjudged her own speed and distance. But there were small fat marsupial mice, and the occasional bush rat, and the slow, stupid possum. She fed well enough, overall, though she found it difficult toward the end to raid the evening roosts of the native birds.

She had no conscious thoughts about it, but the day and evening before the birth she was driven by instinct into a frenzy of killing, and when she finally labored into the den, there were a dozen bush rats and several mice, along with one young possum, all cached in handy locations nearby. Normally, the cat would never eat carrion, preferring to kill her food and eat only when the kill was fresh, but she wouldn't leave her kittens for more than minutes during the first few days of their tiny lives, and the stockpiled menu would keep her journeys to a minimum.

During the first few days after the birthing, she slept a great deal, restoring the enormous strength she would need to hunt for both herself and her kittens. Her milk would sustain them for three or four weeks, even longer, if necessary, but she would require lots of food herself to maintain a strong and healthy supply. She would begin feeding the kittens on solid food at about one month, but the milk would be part of their diet for anywhere from eight to ten weeks.

By the third week, the young male had become the largest of the four kittens, and the most active. He had been the first to open his eyes, a soft blue, and had fumbled his way almost blindly for just on two weeks before the hazy dusk of the den's interior became visible to him. From that very day, it seemed, his progress became more swift; he crawled actively, and at three weeks could stand and move around clumsily on his over-large feet. By the end of thirty days, as his world expanded beyond the limited choices of suckling or sleeping, he quickly became a nuisance in the crowded den.

The mother cat had, at first, used her tongue to keep the tiny kittens clean and their excretions from fouling the den. But as they grew older, she found this no longer possible. By the end of the fifth week, with the fast-growing kittens becoming more noisy and more exuberant in their first stages of play, the soiling of the den forced her to consider a change. The reason was simple enough, though she didn't consciously consider it; the scent was an attraction to predators. It was too risky to stay, and so she moved.

The new den wasn't far away, and it wasn't quite so good a location, but it had the advantage of being almost totally inaccessible to any but the most agile of animals. It was a deep crevasse under a high rock fault, with steep rock all around it and below, and a hair-line track down the rock-face in order to reach it. There was enough room for her growing family, and it would provide security for her kittens when left alone.

It took an hour, each trip, to move the four kittens. Each was gently taken by the scruff of the neck, hoisted in the she-cat's powerful jaws, and half carried, half dragged on the lengthy journey. She growled instructions to each of the other kittens, forcing them to lie quietly and silent until her return.

Then she was on the hunt again, after allowing them to suckle briefly. And this time she sought prey not only for herself, but for the kittens as well. The time had come to begin their weaning, and she returned before the sun had risen enough to touch the valley floor, carrying in her jaws the body of a fresh-killed bush rat.

Of all of them, only the young male took an immediate interest in the bloody carcass. The three female kittens wrinkled their tiny noses as they obeyed the she-cat's persuasion, then struggled to swarm back under their mother toward their milk supply. But the she-cat wouldn't allow that; she lay flat on her belly, keeping them away from her teats, until they returned to nose with their brother at the fresh meat.

The male cat, having licked eagerly at the blood when the rat's body was laid inside the den, became eager for more. He immediately began to use his small, rasping tongue to work off the tiny morsels of meat he could work at with his needle-sharp teeth. It was he, of all of them, who ate the most during their first exposure to adult food.

During the next few weeks, the female cat continued to hunt almost exclusively by night, spending the warm, sun-filled days with her kittens outside the den. The kittens' lives were nearly idyllic. They ate, slept, and chased each other and their mother's tail in the mock-combat playfulness that had become part of their training. But there was discipline, as well, especially when the shadow of a flying predator loomed near them. Then the she-cat would growl her warning, and anything but instant obedience and a speedy dash into the shelter of the overhang would provoke a further growl and a cuff from her mighty forepaw.

The young females were relatively quick to learn such obedience, but the male, his coat now a mottled pattern of ghostly stripes over the clay-colored Siamese background fur, seemed oblivious to the need for such total, immediate reaction to her commands. He would re-enter the den when she growled her dire command, but would be poking an inquisitive nose outside within seconds. And he seemed in perpetual danger of charging headlong down the dangerous rock-face during play, often missing such an accident by a mere whisker.

As greater amounts of meat augmented their milk, the kittens became stronger, more tempted to try their developing muscles and instincts. They interspersed their naps with games of tag and fierce little wrestling matches, games always aimed at development of their skills as stalkers and killers. They would creep silently on tiny padded feet, with their bellies dragging under them, and then launch themselves into a fierce attack on their chosen target.

Usually, for the females, the target was their male litter-mate. And often they ganged up on him in hurtling assaults from behind rocks, under the scrubby little bushes that clung gingerly to the rocks, or from behind the looming bulk of the she-cat. There was no mercy in their attacks, nor in his quick and fierce retaliations. Minute teeth as sharp as needle points and tiny, even-sharper claws were used to full advantage in many of their games.

Other times, it was the mother cat's immense ringed tail that became the target of the ambushes and flashing leaps. The kittens would attack anything that moved, from a windblown stalk of grass to a butterfly shimmering in the sun. The young male actually caught a dragonfly one morning. He tried to call his mother over to view the splendid success, but having caught the insect he didn't know how to hang onto it, and it flew away, badly frightened but alive, before the she-cat answered his demanding squall.

Each of the small females was well-nigh a carbon copy of the old she-cat, except for a hint of Siamese in the boxiness of their striped little faces. At this stage, they were almost inseparable companions, playing, feeding and sleeping together. The male, on the other hand, became more and more of a loner, often wandering by himself in discreet distances from the safety of the den. His Siamese markings had darkened, and except for the faint shadow of stripes that showed in certain lights, he appeared to be a perfect tabby-point Siamese. He thrived on his diet of fresh meat, and grew increasingly aggressive, often boldly forcing his sisters away from the food.

For the she-cat, he had become a constant trial. Several times each day, she was forced to cuff him into submission, or plunge frantically across the rocks to keep him from wandering away into possible danger. Except when they ganged up on him, he bullied his sisters, and he fought with them at the slightest provocation.

His boldness served some good purpose, however, and as the days passed his hunting instincts sharpened steadily. When the female brought home a small, terrified but uninjured marsupial mouse, loosing it to squat quivering with terror before the curious kittens, it was the young male who shrank slowly into position, then pounced expertly to clasp it with his forepaws as he killed it with a bite at the neck. And it was the young male who then defended his kill, slashing at his sisters with drawn claws when they attempted to investigate and share his meal.

During the week that followed, he managed to kill for himself two small skinks and a tiny, legless lizard, each time stalking his prey expertly and leaping to the kill like a miniature tiger.

Gradually, too, the mother cat began to take her litter with her on short trips away from the den, helping them to clamber down the rubble-strewn hillside to where small frogs and lizards near the water provided excellent training for their future hunts alone. But always the male was the boldest, the first to make his kill when stalking something new and different, like the brightly-colored tree frog he surprised on a low branch, and the immature bush rat he caught and toyed with for several minutes before killing it.

SIX

High in a branch-choked ravine below Bull's Head, far to the southwest of Vanity Crossing, a huge, dying gum tree towered above its neighbors. High up, more than fifty feet above the rainforest jungle below, the rotten socket of a lightning-struck branch had deteriorated to leave a deep, protected pocket within the tree. On the other side, a remaining branch and the underbrush below were whitewashed with the droppings of the huge Powerful Owls that nested there.

Inside the hollow, the female owl squatted gently upon the second of her two eggs for that season. The first had been laid four days earlier, and this second one would be the last. The nest itself was a soft mass of feathers, littered with pieces of bone, clumps of fur, and the castings of disgorged material the female's stomach couldn't digest. Similar castings littered the stained ground beneath the perching branch.

As she sat, brooding her eggs, the female picked peckishly at the remains of a possum her mate had brought her during the night. The male huddled sleepily on the branch opposite the nest, one strong talon holding the corpse of a kitten as it lay draped across the branch beside him. He had eaten only a small portion of the kitten, and was hanging onto it for small snacks later in the day.

The mottled, tabby coloring of the kitten was clearly visible through the strong field-glasses that old Dave Bates steadied against his tall walking staff. He murmured a low query at the first sight of it, then stood immobile, studying the owl and its nesting tree for several minutes.

He had been tracking the huge owls for more than a month in the hope of finding their nesting tree, and felt pleased that he had finally accomplished his mission. Although Powerful Owls were relatively common in the more inaccessible regions of the Australian Capital Territory, few of their nesting sites had ever been documented. Dave knew this was partially because owl fanciers didn't want the nests disturbed, and he wasn't about to reveal this location...except to one friend who was a trained zoologist and could be trusted not to cause harm to the owls.

In his years as a dingo-trapper, shearer, drover and wanderer, Dave had come into contact with most native and introduced animals within the Australian bush, but he had only begun to take a specific and conscious interest in them as his own passing years revealed the harsh and often quite irresponsible destruction being caused by the greatest predator, man himself.

He had seen wedge-tailed eagles shot by the dozen and strung upon fence lines in western Queensland and New South Wales, for their widespread but often undeserved reputation as ferocious lamb killers. Not that he denied the fact that the great eagles sometimes did kill infant lambs, he know that in fact they did—occasionally.

But he knew that their continual preying on

rabbits, foxes and young dingoes, as well as feral cats, far outweighed their threat to man and his livestock.

Dave's interest in Powerful Owls had chanced from an encounter with the book *Night-watchmen of Bush and Plain*, the account of naturalist David Fleay's lifetime study of the shy and vividly impressive predator. Fleay had spent much of his life in attempts to study the huge, silent-winged hunters, finally managing, after years of frustration, to breed them in captivity.

Retirement had left old Dave with little to spend his time on but fishing, idle prospecting and roaming his beloved bush and scrub country, so he had taken Fleay's study methods as a guide and begun his own study of the wildlife, especially the Powerful Owls, in the upper Cotter region of the A.C.T.

This particular breeding pair had been together for some time, judging from their dark coloration and enormous size. They were fully mature birds, ranging a territory in which the nesting site was close to the southern boundary. Dave had managed to discover several of their usual camps, identified by the whitewash of their droppings, but until that morning had been unsuccessful in finding their nest.

It had been an arduous job tracking, plunging through dense, overgrown gullies, across spongy, swampy ground and up and down steep ridges in the precarious light of early dawn and evening, when the sitting owls would announce their presence with a peculiar "Woo-Hoo" call.

Their hunting territory, cruised by night on wings made silent by the special softness of fluffy owl feathers, ranged from Bull's Head down into the valley of the Cotter, and most of their prey consisted of the more arboreal animals—the ring-tailed possum and greater glider. But from the scattered litter and pellets disgorged to fall beneath their camps, it became obvious they also took the occasional bird, usually kookaburras. And now, it seemed, the occasional feral cat as well.

The sight of the kitten returned Dave's mind to the incident of the wandering Siamese, Toby, and Dave studied the corpse of the kitten for most of that morning, wondering if it might be the result of Toby's ramblings. The age and size appeared about right, but even with the powerful 10 x 50 binoculars, he couldn't get a good enough look to tell if there was evidence of Siamese breeding. He resolved to make another expedition into the she-cat's territory that week to see if he could find any sign of the litter, perhaps even be lucky enough to catch a glimpse of the kittens.

As the rising noon-day sun improved the light around the owl's perch, Dave unlimbered his camera and affixed the powerful telephoto lens. He then took an entire roll of film, showing the huge male owl, the nesting tree in relation to its surroundings, and the opening to the nest itself. As he took the pictures, the owl paid him no attention at all. Instead, it dipped its head to pick at the corpse of the kitten, ripping off strips of flesh with its mighty beak.

SEVEN

The owl had taken the kitten in the first tinges of daylight, looming down out of the night like some great, ghostly shadow armed with talons of shimmering steel. Only luck had saved the small tomcat from becoming the victim; it had been he that the owl had originally selected as its prey.

All four kittens were in front of the den, squabbling over the remains of a lyrebird that the she-cat had taken from its nest only an hour before. The she-cat had spent most of the night hunting, with unusually poor results until her keen nostrils picked up the trailing scent of the roosting bird. She had stalked it carefully, surely, moving silent through the scrub until the wind favored her, creeping inch by stealthy inch forward until her senses confirmed the bird's shape and position. She was confused at first because the bird was a nesting hen, huddling over her single egg in the large brush nest at the base of a broken gum tree. But the cat's senses gave it a supreme advantage, and her slashing attack drove her through the side entrance of the nest to bring down the hen and kill it quickly. The egg she casually smashed open after the slaying, and she drank the contents before gripping the beautiful corpse in powerful jaws and carrying it home to her kittens.

In the squabble that ensued, the young tomcat knocked aside one of his sisters just as the shadowy form of the owl stooped onto the scene with outstretched talons. The owl tipped its balance left instead of right as the kittens separated, and it was the female who found herself clutched in the razor talons and lifted away.

The kitten's single dying shriek brought the she-cat plunging from the den as her other three kittens struggled to fight their way into it, and she knocked them all sprawling as she reared, hissing her frustrated rage and fear at the departing shape of the great bird.

Actually, the kitten's death was quick; a single searing talon drove through its heart even as the final scream of fear and pain echoed through the still air. Less quickly subdued was the she-cat's anger. She threw herself into the air again and again, clawing at the emptiness as she searched for her missing kitten, and then with angry growls and screams, she herded the remaining kittens into the den and harshly demanded their silence and obedience. During the rest of that day, she was restive and easily roused to anger. At the slightest sound or movement in the scrub around them, she drove the kittens back into the den and prowled the vicinity like a wraith of vengeance. But she was inordinately affectionate, too, with the remainder of her litter, and spent a great deal of time that day in grooming and licking them.

Memory is short in the wild. By nightfall, the incident had lost its significance in the face of a greater need—survival. As the moon rose to silver the silent scrub, the old she-cat led her kittens out to hunt.

Because their climbing abilities were questionable at best, she concentrated mostly on the ground-dwelling denizens of the scrub, and before dawn had stalked and killed several marsupial mice, half a dozen ground-nesting birds and two small lizards.

The kittens did their share, although still too clumsy and incautious to match the deadly skill of their mother. The young tom slew a tiny lizard after a ten-minute stalk carefully watched by the old female, and one of the two remaining female kittens caught a young marsupial mouse that scampered down a tree-trunk almost into the kitten's mouth.

All of them, however, were well on the way to becoming typical examples of the most serious predator of native animals and birds in the Australian bush. More skilled than the marsupial Tiger Cats and the smaller, quite rare Eastern Native Cats—neither being true cats at all—the feral cats directly competed with the native carnivores for food, and also took them as prey whenever the opportunity arose.

Only the young native carnivores were seriously threatened by the introduced cats, but depredations on the larger nesting birds, including such rare and lovely species as the lyrebird, provided justifiable grounds for naturalists to condemn the feral cats as a menace throughout the country. Native predators in the Australian bush are neither numerous nor particularly efficient, especially when compared to the feline perfection of killers like the big female cat.

While her kittens need fear many enemies in their untutored youth, the old cat had no such threats. Only the mighty wedge-tailed eagle or an exceptionally lucky or desperate dingo or feral dog could present her with a serious problem. She was too large for the Powerful Owl to carry off, and most foxes would avoid her anger unless starving.

EIGHT

Dave Bates paused in his tiring trek along the Cotter, planting himself on a large fallen tree trunk to watch the movements of a small rainbow trout in the pool before him. He was unaware, as he stoked his pipe and leaned back to draw contentedly upon it, that he, too, was the object of intense scrutiny. Two sets of eyes only a short distance away were staring unblinkingly at his every move. One pair was slitted in cautious nervousness, and the color of light ale; the second pair was as blue as the sky and wide with interest.

The young tomcat was stirred by his mother's fear and caution, but he had never seen a man before and his own instincts were overshadowed by curiosity. Yet, he didn't move a muscle, except the one that controlled the small twitch in the crook at the end of his light-striped tail.

His two sisters played happily at the mouth of the den, less than 400 yards from where Dave and the cats held their separate watching posts.

The faint breeze brought to the kittens the vaguely disquieting scent of man, but it also carried the assurance that the she-cat was nearby, and that stronger odor in their sensitive little nostrils provided the security that kept them in the open.

Further downwind, out of sight of the mother cat, even had she been looking, lurked an unknown danger—one with far more terrifying implications than the harmless man by the stream.

The sharp eyes of a prowling fox had spied the kittens from a vantage point on the lip of the ravine, and his own excellent nose detected the proximity of the mother cat and the young tom. As he moved slowly against the rising breeze, crouching low, face-to-face with the scrubby cover of the shrubs and rocks, he carefully hid his approach from the kittens. At the same time, he used his nose to reassure himself of the she-cat's location.

The fox smelled human scent, too, but he ignored it. He knew about humans; without the accompanying scent of gunpowder or steel, their scent was no threat to him. He was a long-time resident of the Cotter valley, although usually he ranged further downstream, where he scavenged his living from the garbage cans of the Cotter Reserve and the wasteful habits of campers along the river.

He was past his prime, slowed in his movement and suffering from decaying teeth and vermin-infested fur. His disposition was uncertain at the best of times and his hunting habits varied with it, which accounted for his wandering along the river in the full light of day. He had been driven from his usual haunts by a pack of uncontrolled family dogs the evening before, and he felt both surly and hungry when he sighted the kittens.

Gaunt, with his strong shoulder-bones rearing almost through the fur of his withers, his ruff was a bedraggled parody of the splendid young animal he once had been. Poor weather had reduced the number of campers at the reserve, and lately too many younger, stronger scavengers had beaten him to the meager pickings.

The sight of the two female kittens, plump and tender as two young rabbits and nearly as defenseless, made the old fox slobber and lick his chops. Had the mother cat been with them, he might have reconsidered, since he wasn't quite hungry enough to deliberately court her wrath. But his keen nose told him she was a goodly distance away, and he kept himself reappraised of her presence as he stole cautiously down the rubble-strewn hillside.

His scraggly tail carried low behind him, ears and nose constantly testing the wind for any hint of danger, it took him several minutes to fetch up within leaping distance of the unsuspecting young kittens. He gathered himself back on his haunches, ears flicking forward as he slyly peered through the screen of brush that separated them. Then, as the kittens rolled together in the climax of their own game of stalking each other, he pounced.

The fox's forefeet struck the first kitten and sent it sprawling, just seconds before his slashing jaws snapped the life from the second one.

The scream of his victim was no more than a startled, tenuous squeak, cut off as the fox's blunted teeth crushed its rib-cage and its life. Then he released her and darted his head in a sinuous motion to grasp the other kitten between his jaws. That small female, stunned only briefly by the glancing blow of the fox's paws, let out a squalling bleat of anger and fear, then slashed one tiny forepaw at the blunted muzzle of the fox.

The infant's needle-sharp claws dug into the fox's nose, but the killing lust was on him. Instead of retreating, he opened his jaws and snapped again, and his teeth closed firmly around the kitten's thrashing body. It struggled convulsively for an instant, long enough for a final scream of pain, then was still. The fox dropped it, turning his attention to the other still body as if deciding how best to transport both kills at once. He nuzzled the first, then raised his head to meet the screaming fury of the returning she-cat.

She came out of the low brush like a striped blur of shadow, ears laid back behind an ivory-fanged, wide-open mouth that hissed and snarled her anger. Her fur was raised so that she appeared almost double her true size, and her large forefeet were outstretched with their hooked claws flashing. And right behind her was the young tomcat, his own fur raised and claws unsheathed, but unsure in his own mind whether to join in his mother's attack or run and hide in his fear of the red marauder. The scent of death rose dankly from the limp shapes who had once been his playmates, and despite the white-hot rage of the she-cat, her son could detect tinges of fear in her scent.

Had she arrived a minute earlier, there would have been no battle; the old fox wasn't stupid enough to stand against her without a kill to protect. But his own senses were still heightened from his slaughter, and when she soared out of the bush at him, he dropped his nose close to the ground to save his throat and snapped at the first flashing paw that came his way.

It was an instinctive reaction and he was lucky. His jaws closed on the cat's left forepaw, and with a shake of his head the fox flung her off balance and down on her side. Then he released his grip and drove for her partially exposed throat. But he was too slow. The old cat had twisted even as his jaws let loose their painful hold, and his muzzle found only two flashing feet armed with sickle-shaped razors that cut and caught and cut again across his face.

The cat then grabbed at his ears and neck, hoping to drag him across her to where her vicious dewclaws could do their skilful work. If she could get in under the fox's head and hold her grip, she knew she would easily disembowel him with little real danger to herself. But the old fox knew it too, and he countered by thrusting himself back in order to bring his jaws into play.

She crouched low, batting desperately with her front paws and oblivious to the pain of the crushed forefoot as she tried to keep the fox from getting a fresh bite at her. She lashed out again, and yet again, and each time the fox jerked back his head and snapped with his foaming jaws. The cat, mad with rage and pain, slashed out, then reared to launch into a rampant attack on the fox's face. But he was too ready, and for once too quick. He retreated a step as she lunged, and as her weight hit her injured forefoot, she screamed with the agony and fell heavily forward, off balance and out of control.

It was the move the fox had been awaiting; he lunged forward in the instant, his jaws closing high on the cat's exposed back. Beneath his blunt teeth, he could feel the ribs begin to crunch, and he levered himself backward to throw up his head in the final, spine-breaking snap that would end it.

Then a diminutive bundle of spitting, slashing fury landed squarely on his head. He opened his mouth in a yelp of angry pain as tiny, needle-sharp claws laced across one eye and into the sensitive areas of his nose.

The small tomcat had, temporarily, conquered his fear. He leaped to the attack again as the fox threw himself backwards. The fox tossed the young cat off to land sprawling behind him, then swiveled to spring upon the small gray body as it twisted to regain balance. However, the full weight of the mother cat landed squarely upon his shoulders and he gave another angry, terrified yelp.

From then on, it was entirely the cat's fight. She rode him as if she were a bronc-buster in a rodeo, hanging onto his ruff with both front feet—despite the pain—and clawing rapidly and deep along his flanks with her hind paws.

Sometimes her injured forepaw lost its grip, but her exceptional balance kept her upright as her threshing claws continued their fearsome slaughter of the fox's mangy pelt.

Her claws ripped and tore, flaying the beast's hide from belly to backbone, shoulder to heaving flank. And as she rode him, she screamed out her fury and hurt and rage, and her screams blended with the fox's anguished yelps as he turned and ran for the thickest brush in sight.

The cat's teeth and claws were fastened deep in his neck and ruff, but she knew there was no killing power in her position. What she wanted was to throw him off balance, get him down where she could find his vitals with her deadly hind-claws and rip open his thin-furred belly.

The small tomcat stood in frightened awe at the spectacle, his own bravery gone as quickly as it had come, knocked from him with his breath when he fell. His mother and the large red fox became a mingled blur in his sight as the fox spun and scrambled to reach the thicker scrub below the den.

And then it was over, with the injured fox fleeing for his very life down the river gorge and the old she-cat lying twisted in pain after being brushed from his back by a heavy tangle of thicket. She moaned aloud in her torment, but still her ears were laid back in rage and her sharp teeth gnashed through the ropes of saliva at her jaws.

When the young cat approached her, tentative and afraid, she soothed quickly; her voice softened to moans and grunts of pleasure as she tried to lift herself to lick at him.

But the scrub had finished what the fox began. Her spine was beyond repair and a smashed rib had driven deeply into her lungs. Even as she licked at her sole surviving kitten, trickles of foamy blood began to stain her side and a reddened froth formed on her lips with each cough of departing life.

The young cat tried to snuggle against her.

Then his ears caught the sound of approaching footsteps, and he ran to crouch in immobile terror beneath a low-slung bush.

NINE

Dave Bates saw the tiny, huddled form of the male kitten, but he ignored it, consciously keeping his eyes averted as he studied the scene of carnage.

Leaning on his staff, he panted heavily, wondering at his own foolishness in charging so recklessly up the slope to check out the sounds of the battle. His old heart thundered, and the noise of it pulsed in his ears as he looked down on the broken bodies of the two female kittens.

The rank scent of the dog fox wrinkled his nose, and the evidence of the fox's attack was strewn all around the den.

Dave walked closer to peer down at the still

body of the female cat, already the object of swarming bush flies. The froth of blood around her muzzle and the curious twisting of her body made the injuries obvious, but the scattered masses of fox fur were testimony to her fearless battle.

After a minute, Dave walked over to the mouth of the den and stooped to peer into the darkness. Then he crouched, and after poking inside with his staff to ensure it held no unpleasant surprises, he crawled as far inside as he could and emerged a minute later with handfuls of the rubbish from within. He cursed softly at the lyrebird feathers, then rose and reached absently into his pocket for his pipe.

Throughout, the kitten held its place, staring with unblinking eyes at this mammoth intruder. He shook with shock and fear, but curiosity returned as his breath slowed, and he continued to scrutinize the man's movements.

Counseling himself not to frighten the kitten further, Dave watched it out of the corner of his eye. Then, slowly, moving to where a large boulder offered him a seat, he proceeded to light and draw on his pipe.

A portion of his mind told him to try and capture the kitten, who was really too young to have much chance of survival in its orphaned state. But the rest of Dave's mind, the thinking portion that could reject emotionalism, said no. It would be damfoolish to expect that the cat could ever be satisfactorily tamed. Young as it was, and perhaps too young to survive the rigorous demands of a feral life, it was already far too old to accept domesticity.

Dave knew the folly of trying to make a pet from a wild creature. And he knew that the blood of the Siamese Toby, strained through generations of domesticity, would mean nothing where this young cat was concerned. It was a wild beast, as wild as anything in the bush, and yet...

He could neither kill it, nor bear the knowledge that it would almost certainly starve, so he had to at least try to capture it. But how? At his age, he doubted if he could run the kitten down, although he knew its stamina was not great. Even the mighty cheetah could only hold a full running gait for minutes before heart and lungs demanded a rest, and this kitten was already wearied by the shock of his battle and the experience of so much sudden, frightening death.

Dave thought about it for some time, looking everywhere but at the blue eyes which never left him. Then he rose, moving slowly again, and began to circle around the kitten's position.

He moved with infinite patience, a step and then a pause, and then another step. Twice he walked a full circle around the tiny cat, which turned right along with him, never for an instant taking its bright blue eyes from his movements. With each circle Dave drew somewhat closer, although the rocky, sloping ground made the approach difficult.

This just might work, he thought...too soon.

As he began the third circle, the kitten's nerve broke; Dave was too close and the cat couldn't accept it. Tearing his gaze from the looming, gigantic figure, the tomcat slithered under the spreading branches and faded back into the tangled brush. Dave took his chance, diving frantically in a bid to grasp the kitten before it ploughed through into the open. But he failed.

As he rolled to his feet, the kitten emerged from the far side of the bush and sped straight away down the rubble-strewn hillside, moving like a flash of gray light. Dave plunged after him, thinking as he did that it was a waste of time, and sure of it when the cat reached the low ground near the stream and dived straight into a cluster of blackberry bushes.

"You're right now, lad," Dave muttered as he skidded to a stop before he, too, slammed into the viciously hooked thorns of the barrier. "There's no bloody way I'm coming in *there* after you."

And having decided, he turned on his heel and walked away.

The small kitten lay for better than two hours under the bramble shelter of the blackberries, shivering occasionally with fearful memories of the fox and the gigantic animal that had followed it. His mottled fur gave him perfect camouflage. A passing mob of wallabies, stirred from their afternoon nap by the commotion earlier, passed within yards of him without realizing his presence, and two magpies played and scolded at each other in a tree above his head without even knowing he was beneath them.

But even after his senses had confirmed that both his enemies were gone, the kitten lay fearful, his tiny heart thundering in his ears. It wasn't until the fading light of late afternoon spun pools of shadow around the rocks and bushes that he crept from his hiding place. Slowly, moving each paw with infinite caution, he crept from shadow to shadow, cover to cover, until he reached the scene of his mother's death. There, he also found the chilled bodies of his sisters.

Throughout the evening he stayed huddled within sight of his mother's fly-blown body, his senses offended by the scent of death and the rankness of the fox smell, his need for parental closeness over-shadowing his fears. But after a time, as the rising moon provided a new light and his small stomach made its own demands, he moved away from the carnage and the den.

TEN

The kitten's hunting was hampered by his fear. The sounds of the bush seemed louder, more strange than he had ever noticed when hunting by his mother's side. At each new shriek of bird or rustle of small feet in the undergrowth, the kitten thrust himself instinctively into the shadows, freezing into immobility except for a slight tremble of fear until the sound was either identified or had passed. And with his fear grew his hunger, difficult to slake while he jumped and shied at every sound and shadow.

It was nearly daybreak before he managed to slay a small, careless tree frog after a clumsy but lucky stalk.

At sunrise he returned to the den, but the insect scavengers were busy and the still-strong odors of fox and death were too much for him. With a final sniff at his mother's stiffened body, he turned away and began to wander upriver, searching for somewhere safe to lie up while he rested.

He was tired, footsore and confused, but he wandered for several hours until he found a hollow gum log which offered shelter. Shelter, and more...he managed to surprise the two small marsupial mice that lived in the log, and in their panic one blundered within reach of the kitten's striking paws. He ate quickly, ravenously, without wasting a single morsel of skin, gut or gristle. Then he curled up and slept for the remainder of the day, his body giving way to his exhaustion.

He woke with the evening to fresh hunger and an equally strong loneliness, and prowled through the night like a small gray ghost in the moonlight. A hungry ghost, because his loneliness and fear made him invariably leap into hiding and his partial training wasn't sufficient to keep him consistently fed. Fortunately for the young cat, however, the weather stayed fine during his first days alone, and the old female's choice of territory assured him of sufficient potential prey; more than enough to give him at least a fighting chance at survival. Many a day, though, saw him seeking his bed with a growling, still-empty stomach.

Experience eventually taught him what the old cat hadn't lived long enough to teach. One memorable night he paused in his over-cautious stalking of a large bush rat and watched, enthralled, as the animal dined fastidiously on the eggs of a ground-nesting bird. The kitten killed the rat while its attention was thus diverted, and after filling his own stomach for the first time in days, he tested the flavor of the broken eggs. He didn't fancy the taste, especially, but he remembered it. The knowledge would be valuable later, in times when hunger made him less choosy.

As nesting time for the myriad ground-nesting birds increased, he became highly adept at stalking the hens, and gradually began to retreat from the near-starvation of his first weeks. Then, sheer hunger had forced him to prowl both day and night in search of any morsel that would help fill his shrunken belly.

Eventually, he began to fill out once more. His feet toughened and his muscles responded to the long, arduous days and nights on the hunt. He learned by himself to climb trees, and his health responded well to the increased feeding prospects that a semi-arboreal life provided. He learned that roosting birds were easy prey at night, and that eggs were to be found in aerial nests as well as on the ground.

Once the magpies began their nesting, he gradually abandoned his daytime hunting. They made his life a continuous torment, and they seemed to be everywhere in the valley. Each time he passed a nesting site in daylight, it was to receive a swishing, pecking attack from one of the large, black-and-white birds. They would follow him, swooping to dive-bomb him, but they never got quite close enough to catch. And as quickly as he was driven from one territory, it seemed, he strayed into another, and a fresh attack.

But at night, in the shadowy light of the moon, when the birds huddled sleepily on their roosts and in the nests, he climbed silently into the tall river gums and slaughtered them in their beds. They were easy prey, and filling. The young cat found himself in direct competition for such morsels with a roving native cat, and one night he chanced on one of the spotted, arboreal killers while it was engrossed in raiding a magpie nest. Normally, the young cat would flee for his own life from a cunning slayer almost his own size, but this night he felt ravenous, and in a brilliant display of bluff and deception he frightened the native animal from its prey and enjoyed the meal himself.

He was less fortunate in his observations of a young dog fox. The russet, brush-tailed marauder's bat-like ears picked up some slight movement made by the cat, and the fox immediately abandoned his stealthy approach to a small, brown marsupial mouse and bounded toward what he obviously considered more substantial prey. It was easy enough for the cat to flee into the nearest tree, but if he'd been caught on more open ground it would have been his death.

As necessity sharpened his hunting instincts and abilities, he didn't generally go hungry with the coming of dawn, but his growing body weight required constant nourishment and he was hard put to stay uniformly well fed. Still, he was winning, however slowly, and each passing week gave him new confidence, new lessons, and increased skill as a predator.

As he grew, his Siamese characteristics became increasingly pronounced. He had his sire's distinctive, blocky facial structure, and in some lights almost the identical base color. But the female cat's strong genes had provided a muted blotchiness of coat, and the overshadowing of blotches and stripes seemed to float his entire body into shadow patterns when the light dimmed. He had also gained from the she-cat some of the massive bone structure which would make him a far larger cat than his sire at maturity, provided he survived that long.

Survival, for the growing kitten, was often a matter of sheer luck and flickering, speedy reflexes. His education from the female had ended too early to grant him the total overview of the dangerous world in which he lived. Without her protection, there was little room for mistakes.

The first native cat he'd encountered had come within a whisker of eating the kitten for breakfast. While the young cat tried to decide if the spotted killer was relative or enemy, the older and more experienced marsupial carnivore had no such indecision. It was only a remarkable turn of speed and a vivid and detailed knowledge of his own territory that allowed the young cat to flee the encounter at a pace the native cat couldn't quite match. After that, the kitten regarded every such animal as a potential threat, although he quickly outgrew the need for such caution.

The valley provided generally good hunting for the young cat through his first winter and the spring that followed. He was incredibly lucky, but he had a quick and willing mind and soon learned which denizens of the valley could be a threat to him.

He feared the foxes, relatively rare as they were. He ignored the gray kangaroos and the wallabies, too large and speedy to be considered prey. The burly wombat who laired a mile upstream from the Vanity Crossing was a surly fellow, a fully mature adult male, and the kitten knew better than to bother him. There was a family of feral pigs that ranged near the upper edge of the Cotter Reservoir, but after he'd been chased over relatively open ground by the sow, the young cat avoided the region.

He learned about snakes mostly by instinct, and although he encountered them almost daily, he gave each one a wide berth. The smaller reptiles, without the threat of poison in their fangs, he considered fair and usually easy prey.

He retained his wariness of the silent-winged Powerful Owl long after he had reached a size where the huge bird was no longer a serious threat, and subsequent to one brief, harrowing experience in which a wedge-tailed eagle missed him by a whisker, he kept a wary eye skyward whenever he found himself in open ground by daylight.

The arrival of his first proper summer brought a new and easy food source for the young cat, although his mother wouldn't have approved. Without her rigid discipline and inbred caution, the young cat accepted it eagerly as a varied resource of his range. Every weekend of warm weather brought increasing numbers of campers and picnic parties who found the cooling waters of the Cotter and the shady sandbanks at Vanity Crossing a veritable godsend after the mugginess of the city. They came in cars, panel-vans and on motorcycles, but all had one thing in common—they were unbelievably messy. Their departure each evening left behind a rubble of beer and soft-drink cans, along with paper litter in astonishing amounts. And food! Pieces of charred steak, bones from steaks and chops, discarded frankfurters and sausage ends, unfinished sandwiches. The young cat didn't need much encouragement to learn the value of a Sunday evening visit, and he eagerly harvested the feast.

He learned, also, that it was wisest to be on the scene as the last human visitor departed; otherwise the semi-tame kookaburras and squawking crows would beat him to the spoils. But it was a good feeding place, partially for the abundant rubbish and partially for other scavengers, like possums, which were prey for him.

The strong memories he retained of his mother's death and of Dave Bates' proximity at the time kept him shy of people, and he remained well hidden from any human visitors, even when poor hunting had made his stomach shrink and growl and the temptation of the discarded goodies was strong within him. More than the people, he feared their pets. On various occasions, family dogs that chanced on his presence gave him a fearful and heart-lurching run before he shook them off or escaped to the safety of a tall gum tree.

As he approached his full size—although it would be years before he gained the solidness of bone and muscle to bring him the full weight of peak condition—he became less and less afraid of the normal perils in the bush. Only the foxes and dogs and the occasional wedge-tailed eagle presented much serious danger. The native marsupial cats, bloodthirsty as weasels and equally ferocious, weren't large enough to threaten him, and dingoes that close to the haunts of man were rare.

He still wandered a great deal up and down the valley, but his range centered on Vanity Crossing that summer, where he was assured of an easy meal from either the trash or the other scavengers it drew. To his credit, however, not once was he seen by his unknowing providers. Sometimes people walked within centimetres of his camouflaged form, but as he lay unmoving and silent they never even suspected his presence.

Dave Bates, of course, knew about the young cat, but on his many visits to the area he found only the occasional track in the sand. He wasn't surprised at not finding the cat himself, and was content to use the search for him as an excuse to wander the river with a fishing rod and his camera. But finally, and coincidentally, on a day exactly a year from their first meeting, Dave got a look at the young cat, and it was the animal's carelessness which allowed it.

Cats are curious, and this young, half-wild tomcat was typical of his breed. One of his better tricks involved the following of fishermen on their way along the Cotter. The stream provided beautiful if not over-productive trout water, and each weekend brought at least one fisherman to stroll along its banks. It was a fisherman who provided the cat with his first taste of fresh-caught fish. The man left his catch, carefully wrapped in wet newspaper, tucked in the shade of a large streamside rock, while he searched farther downstream for another of his quarry. The curious young cat, following through the dawn light after a poor night on the hunt, found the fish easily and took appropriate advantage. When the fisherman returned for his trophy, it had been reduced to a skeleton and a head, buried in rags of tattered newsprint. Since then, the young cat had stolen several fish from fishermen who really should have known better.

When Dave Bates heard the tale from one angry fisherman, he was at first inclined to disbelieve it. Then he began to think a fish might provide him with a slim chance of photographing the young cat. Dave was torn in his feelings about the animal, knowing as he did the tremendous impact feral cats made upon the native marsupials and birds. But he was as curious as the tomcat he sought, and he wondered how much of the Siamese heritage might have survived maturity.

And he was bored. Retirement provided little excitement in his life. So the next afternoon he set forth with his camera, fishing gear, and a tin of sardines as additional bait. He had no illusions about his chances of success. He suspected he could spend several days or even weeks at the task, and still fail.

First he found a suitable location, one where the cat would be forced into the open if he made a try for the fish and one where Dave himself was assured of a good place of concealment for his camera work. He picked two sites, both of them near the junction of Condor Creek with the larger Cotter. He resolved to try each one for a week, and if he couldn't get lucky there, he would devote another week to lurking at the picnic grounds at Vanity Crossing.

He set his bait, sardines and trout, and then with the patience born of years in the bush, he settled back to wait.

The first week he shot some excellent pictures of kookaburras, a shy native cat, and various other birds and reptiles...but he never saw the feral tomcat. Four days into the second week, Dave added a young fox to his growing list of models.

On the fifth day, Dave was close to abandoning his bait to a couple of very interested magpies when the birds suddenly flared skyward, the bush ringing with their raucous danger signals. Dave held himself still, his gaze searching the ground near the fish which he'd hung on a low branch, but he could see nothing.

Without moving his head, he began to sweep the area, using a steady, nearly unblinking gaze. He knew it was more likely that he would catch movement or a change in shadow-shapes with his peripheral vision. A direct stare would focus too sharply, lose too much perspective, while gentle, slow movements would pick out detail without conscious thought, even allowing for the often-amazing camouflage of a wild creature.

Above, the black-and-white birds continued their screaming, but try as he would, Dave could see nothing approach the bait. As he cautiously swept his gaze along the low brush, a heavy cloud formation moved in to obscure the sun, and he was glad for a camera with automatic exposure. Nonetheless, he glanced down at it just to check, and when he looked up, the cat was there.

A second shift of the high-moving cloud occurred, and the resultant shafts of direct sunlight revealed the underlaid striping of the young tom's coat beneath grayish-tan outer fur.

Dave stifled a gasp at the unexpected size of the animal. It had reached full height and possessed the sleek, boxy body shape of its Siamese sire, combined with the bulk of its massive mother. For a moment, Dave could only stare at the feral cat as it slowly paced toward the fish, and he stifled a chuckle at the cat's haughty disdain for the screaming din overhead.

Finally, remembering the purpose of the exercise, Dave focused his camera. At the first exposure, the clicking sound brought the sinewy figure to a sharp halt, and it stood like a shadow with its large ears and blue eyes straining to locate the source of the sound. Dave just sat there, hardly breathing, as the cat stood immobile. Then it returned its attention to the fish, and Dave recocked the camera, using as little movement as he could manage. It seemed to him that the lever fairly screamed as it moved the film ahead, but the cat didn't seem to hear.

He risked another picture, and the sound of the shutter seemed, in his own ears, like a gunshot. But the cat merely started into alertness for a second before turning to bat at the dangling fish with one forepaw. Dave wound the lever again and took a third exposure, and this time the cat turned to stare at him. He could see the long whiskers trembling in the sunlight; otherwise, the cat looked like a statue. Even the large eyes, luminous in the sunlight, might have been carved from glass.

The cat turned once more to the fish, rearing up to paw it from the branch and bring it down between dark-striped forepaws. A slash with one paw opened the fish from gills to tailfin, and Dave took four more pictures as the cat crouched over its purloined prey and began to pry at the meat with flickering movements of its raspy tongue.

Dave became engrossed. He'd never before bothered to watch the manner in which a cat fed, and was mildly surprised to see that it didn't actually bite at the meat, but used the roughness of its tongue to rasp slivers of flesh away from the bones. Dave took several more pictures before he ran out of film.

He muttered a silent curse and shrugged slightly back into his covert, determined to change film even through he doubted he could manage without frightening the cat away. The rewind lever sounded like a noisy whirr, the fanfare as he tore the foil from the fresh cassette sounded louder yet, but he managed with fumbling fingers to reload his camera as the cat concentrated on its meal.

Dave shot several more pictures as the now well-fed animal began toying with the remains of the fish. The cat grasped the skeleton in its forepaws, flung it into the air and then grabbed it again before it struck the ground. His movements were exactly those of a house cat playing with a piece of crumpled paper.

Mesmerized, Dave grew careless. He showed the slightest motion as he advanced the film, but it was enough. The cat froze, eyes and ears homing in on the movement. Then a flickering stray breeze carried Dave's scent to him, and the cat's mind reacted so transparently, even Dave could see it. First, the cat shrank down close to the ground, his eyes narrowed and his ears flung back against his skull, the muscles in his haunches trembling as he looked from side to side.

And then he was gone.

There wasn't a sound. There wasn't so much as a ripple in the low underbrush. The cat simply vanished. Disappeared. So quickly, Dave missed it entirely. It was as if the cat had never been there, except for the shredded fish and, ultimately, the evidence on Dave's film.

The cat hadn't reacted specifically to the memory of the man who had chased him a year before. His reminiscence of the mother cat's death and the incidents with it didn't exist as such a specific thing. But what remained was a sensory impression, a half-instinctive reaction to the stimulus of Dave's personal aroma. The cat didn't even know why it spelled danger, and he didn't wait around long enough to investigate. Survival was his guide, and survival rules forced him to flee.

He traveled a mile downstream, moving at top speed for the time required to get him out of sight. Then he dropped to a long, sinuous lope as the immediacy of the incident faded.

By evening he'd forgotten it entirely, being far more concerned about the stalk of a small frilled lizard he stumbled upon. The lizard spied him and tried to flee, but not before the cat's initial pounce. It wasn't one of his best attacks, however, and the uninjured lizard rose from between his front paws to froth out its wide neck skin and rear up to hiss at him.

The cat circled the reptile for several turns, confused. Finally, he simply walked off and left it. He wasn't hungry enough to brave the defense mechanism he found so puzzling.

ELEVEN

As the young tomcat moved into his second year of growth, his budding sexual maturity forced upon him an increased need to wander from the home territory he had maintained since kittenhood. Gradually, he began to work his way farther and farther downstream, following the eastern shore where the waters of the river broadened into the beginning of the Cotter reservoir.

He was now a large cat; though still not fully grown, he weighed in at nearly a dozen pounds and every ounce of it was solid bone and strong, flexible muscle. He was in prime condition, having mastered his survival lessons and learned as much as his mother could have taught him. Seldom, now, did he miss his prey once his careful, feline stalk had begun. He slaughtered nesting birds both on the ground and in the trees, slew young possums and sugar-gliders with consummate skill and ease, and varied his diet at will on marsupial mice, small rodents, and lizards.

Surprised on his kill one morning by a small dog, a terrier crossbreed that wasn't much bigger than the cat, his instincts to run were over-shadowed by another instinct...that of defending his kill.

The cat backed away at first, placing the carcass of the lyrebird between them. Then he half-faced the cautious intruder and raised the fur on his neck and shoulders in an instinctive attempt to make himself look larger than he really was.

Ears flattened against his skull, his ruff and tail fluffed out as far as they would go, the cat began a series of rocking motions, taking his weight first upon one forefoot and then the other. As the starving dog moved closer, the cat began to growl and gnash his teeth, saliva dripping from his fangs as he worked himself up into a frenzy of rage.

For the small dog it was all quite confusing. He was only about a year old, and his experiences with cats during that first year had led him to believe that they would always run from him. Besides, he was drooling with insatiable hunger, not having fed in more than three days.

The terrier was another victim of human callousness. Taken as a free puppy because his crossbreeding made him valueless, he'd been well enough cared for in a Canberra home until his approaching maturity made him assert his own personality and authority. It is something all male dogs do, but his indifferent owner didn't know that, or didn't care. Faced with a dog that, in his mind, had dared to growl at him and was therefore vicious, the owner simply decided it was somehow the dog's fault. So he drove out along the road to Brindabella one night and dumped the dog into the ditch. Dogs were wild animals by nature, the man thought, never realizing the young terrier's chances of survival were so slight as to be negligible.

The dog had starved for the first few days, then managed to capture a small frog and then a slightly larger lizard. When it met the tomcat, all thoughts of caution were driven from it by simple hunger.

It was an uneven contest from the start. The cat was stronger, more fierce, and since it was his kill rather than the dog's, he was more certain of his ground. When the small brown-and-white dog raced at him, yapping bravely, the cat didn't retreat. He attacked.

Claws slashing like scimitars, he rose into the air in a plunging leap that carried him straight onto the dog's shoulder. With his fore-paws hooked in, he swiveled until he could get his rear feet into action, clawing at the dog's flanks and rump and growling and spitting his anger at the same time.

The terrified dog turned tail and ran, desperately seeking to get the screaming, clawing monster off his back. He charged into some low sheoaks, then down under a low-hanging log, and finally straight into a blackberry thicket. The cat gave it up, then, more because of the distance they had traveled from the still-warm corpse of the lyrebird than because he felt like abandoning the fight.

The dog continued its flight, blood streaming from wounds all over its body, until it was turned by the waters of the reservoir. Weakened by its own starvation as much as the loss of blood, it fell into a swampy area some distance along, and the chill night air brought with it a cold and flux that killed the small dog three days later. He would have died of starvation anyway; it simply would have taken longer.

The cat, after his meal, continued on his ramblings, and later that night he cut the track of a female cat beside the pondage of the large reservoir.

The she-cat wasn't in heat; his decision to follow the scent was based more on curiosity than anything else. Since the death of his mother and sisters, the young tom had seldom encountered one of his own species. His feelings were tinged with wariness, but there was also a need to find the female cat, to establish some kind of contact.

It took him a day and a half before a wispy breeze took him off the scent trail and across a rocky spur near the water to where he knew the female would be. He rounded the edge of the outcrop, moving silently and with caution, but it was obvious at first sight that the female knew where and what he was.

She was a large cat, and very old. She was mostly a muddle of tan and blotchy yellow, with only a hint of rings on her fat tail. She was also slightly pregnant, and certainly in no mood to accept a roving tomcat on the territory she'd staked out for her denning. As the young cat moved slowly closer, she crouched low to the ground, her fur fluffed up, her tail lashing out her warnings, her throat issuing forth growling hisses.

She knew about tomcats, having dealt with many of them since she had been dumped in the bush with her first litter almost twelve years before. She had been a kitten herself at the time, having mated during her first heat cycle, and she'd no inkling of the harsh survival laws of the bush when her owner had thrown her from the moving car, with her litter, in a large cardboard box.

Two of her kittens had died in the fall and the rest starved to death as the mother, herself injured, found it impossible to get enough food to keep herself alive and her milk supply strong enough to nourish them. She had almost died herself, and emerged from the ordeal as a walking skeleton, her fur dulled and ridden with parasites and her injured leg barely able to bear her weight. But it had been a lucky season, a good summer with the marsupial mice breeding furiously and an abundance of bird life. She had survived, and gradually learned the same lessons as the young tomcat she faced.

During the years, she had produced litters as regularly as circumstances allowed, losing virtually all of them to other predators, including roving tomcats. This would be her last litter, and her smallest. Only one small germ of fresh life within her had been created at her mating, as age lessened her fertility.

The young cat knew nothing of this, of course. And although her hostility was obvious, he had no experience to guide him in the etiquette of the situation. So he continued his wary approach, even though she bared her fangs in a sibilant hissing, then spat angrily and tossed her head.

He stopped, shock still, but with one forepaw lifted in an almost curious gesture as he stared at her. The female was a portrait in fierceness, her eyes amber ice, her thick tail switching angrily. With her ruff and cheeks fluffed out, she looked twice her size.

The young tom stared at her, unmoving and with his foot still poised. His instincts told him to withdraw, but other inner feelings tried to force some form of contact. Softly, deep in his throat, a thin, mewling sound began to develop. It traced a way through his muscular throat and out between shining, ivory teeth to cross the hostile air between the two cats. Nothing! He whined again, instinctively moving his head to one side in a partial gesture of pleading, of submission. Had the female not been pregnant, it would have been enough to stave off her anger and hostility, but her own instincts were too strongly against the tom.

He slowly lowered his foot, shaking his head as he cocked one ear and looked at her. She spat again, reaching up with a forepaw to claw at the air. Her tail began to lash more quickly; if he didn't retreat she would have to attack. Her claws were outstretched and gleaming, her ears laid back flat against her skull, and her teeth drooled with saliva. The young cat should have retreated, but instead he moved one step closer.

The old she-cat launched herself like a missile in a screaming, slashing attack that the tomcat could not counter. One lightning-fast forepaw raked across his forehead, the claws ripping through the tender skin at the base of his ear. He reared back in anger and pain, his own nape rising in angry bristles as he spat his indignation. But she was larger and her attack drove him back two paces before he could regain his balance. It was only a small retreat, but it was enough. He couldn't be the aggressor in such a situation and the she-cat knew it.

Encouraged, she drove more strongly into the attack, launching herself even as the young cat found his footing. Again he was forced back, this time half-turned as he raised himself upright and began to slash back at her.

She struck his poorly-protected shoulder and he turned further, no long interested in anything except escape. Her claws slashed his flank, and although she didn't pursue him more than a dozen steps, her voice carried the fight to him until he was fifty yards away. Then she turned and stalked away on her own trail, satisfied with her accomplishment.

The young tom continued on the run for nearly half a mile, not bothering to try and sort out the smells or sounds of the bush around him. He was angry and he was hurt, and not a little confused by his reception.

Except for the rip at the base of his ear, his injuries were really quite insignificant, and after a time he stopped and began to groom the ear injury with a gentle forepaw, wincing each time he touched it too hard.

A few hours later he had pushed the incident from his conscious mind, intent instead on his search for a meal.

The other small scratches took only days to heal, and within a week the ear had developed a thick scab. The tom kept moving, and didn't encounter the old she-cat's sign again as he carried on down the shore of the reservoir.

TWELVE

The first pale streaks of daylight were tingeing the sky one morning when a slight splashing sound stopped the hungry tomcat in his tracks. His ears cocked to listen and his pupils grew larger as he strained with all of his senses to identify the sound at the edge of the reservoir.

The lapping of the water against the undercut roots of a huge old gum tree had created a small muddy shelf, overhung by the buttressing of the tree itself. As the cat slunk up on the landward side, a slight movement on the shelf drew his gaze and he began a steady, silent approach using the shadow of the tree for cover. When he was within striking distance, he could see quite plainly the smooth, moist shape of the creature that lay half submerged on the muddy shelf.

His great eyes picked out each detail without difficulty in the slowly strengthening light, and the tomcat took in every aspect of the unusual creature, from its queer, beak-like muzzle across a body covered in sleek, water-blackened fur to a broad, flattened tail that stirred gently in the shallows. The creature's eyes were hidden in the depth of the fur, and the cat could detect no suspicion in its movements, no hint that it had either heard or sensed his presence.

Hunger spoke loudly, then, and almost without conscious thought the cat launched himself into a diving attack on the platypus.

His aim was perfect, but as his paws hit the dense, sopping fur, he recoiled instinctively, and that was all the advantage the platypus required. Still silent, it lurched ahead with the driving power of its webbed feet, churning up the mud as it dove forward off the edge of the bank toward the deeper water. The cat couldn't find a grip on the slippery back, and when his own paws began to claw at the water, he let go entirely. All he saw as he struggled and spat his way back to dry land was a dark, shadowy figure sliding easily out of sight.

The thoroughly frustrated and baffled young cat uttered a half-hearted yowl of frustration, then leapt on a dry fallen leaf and slashed at it with his claws. It was almost half an hour, a time of shivering and shaking himself and using his rough tongue and forepaws as grooming aids, before he looked reasonable again and felt comfortable enough to continue his search for food. He threw a disgusted look at the mudbank where the departing ripples of the platypus had long since vanished, and lifted his head to yowl his anger.

But the sound caught in his throat as his broad ears perked to the sound of a faint, yodeling cat scream that trailed thinly through the morning air. He stood silent for several minutes, every sense tuned to that distant, somehow melodic call, and when it was finally repeated he answered with an instinctive screech of his own. Then he turned and began trotting steadily along the shore of the reservoir, head high and ears perked.

Half an hour later, he leapt to a large, lightning-blasted stump and poised himself daintily before lifting his head to yowl his query at the sunrise. He was close and he knew it, but he couldn't accurately pinpoint the alluring sound he'd been following. After a moment, he screamed again, and this time a faint but definite answer filtered down from the bush farther along the reservoir. He hopped down from the stump and moved forward, his every sense alerted by the imperative summons. It was a sound he'd never heard before, but instinct guided his response despite the caution that lurked from his last encounter with a female cat.

This one, however, was younger. And more important, she was at the peak of her heat cycle and was actively seeking a mate. She was a lithe gray shape in the dawn, a cat only three generations feral but already almost as wild as the young tomcat's mother had been. When he approached, slowly and cautiously, she mewed at him enticingly and shrugged her dainty shoulders as she sniffed with him nose to nose. They circled deliberately for a moment, each using eyes and nose and whiskers to ascertain the specifics of the other. Then she turned coyly away from him and threw herself to the ground in a playful roll.

When he followed, she pawed lightly at his face before surging to her feet and dashing playfully away from him. He chased her, but each time he closed the distance she would lithely twist away, turning to bat at him with sheathed claws and mew her small sounds of affection and encouragement. Though younger than he, she had already thrown two litters. Thus, she knew the formalities and the rituals which must be followed.

Turning away once more, she led the young tomcat in a seemingly leisurely gambol along the edge of the water, always staying just far enough ahead to make him chase her, but never so far ahead that he might lose interest. The ritual was necessary to build up in the tom the same strength of desire that already inflamed the gray cat. All thoughts of hunger were forgotten. He threw his entire spirit into following the female's blatant enticements. And, as planned, his mating desires built higher as she played and rolled and flung herself against him. They rounded a shallow covert of thicket on the edge of the valley, and suddenly both were halted by a screeching, challenging yowl from the bush ahead. The tomcat immediately found his hackles rising in answer to the sound, but his companion's reaction was a plaintive yet demanding wail of her own.

From out of the bush, moving in a tall, stiff-legged hostility, stalked a scraggly, lean old tomcat, his lips wrinkled in challenge as he faced up to the younger male. An aged warrior with one ear almost torn away in some long-ago battle, his scars showed plainly through the scruffy fur on his hindquarters. Brindle in color, he looked like a miniature tiger as he strode purposefully toward the young tomcat. The warrior's tail slashed at the air and his whiskers and nostrils quivered with eager expectation.

As they approached each other, both males hunched up their shoulders and turned half sideways, ears laid back and mouths gaping as they screamed their challenges again and again.

The young cat was larger, and if anything somewhat more fit, but he lacked the fighting experience of the wise old tom, and this became apparent both to the older male and the sleek gray female, who immediately began to posture herself provocatively as if she were thoroughly prepared to sit back and enjoy the pending battle. In answer to the striped tom's snarls, the younger male issued screaming yowls of his own, saliva drooling from his lips as he laid back his ears and circled to keep the other cat from a direct attack position.

But even as he searched for an opening, his lack of fighting experience allowed his opponent a first advantage, and the striped brindle cat leaped in quickly to slash at the young tom's poorly-protected flank. The old cat's claws, razor sharp and powered by stringy, solid muscles, slashed a vicious track across the younger cat's rump, and the young tom backed away with a squall of pain and anger. Whereupon, the old cat buckjumped with both front paws hooked toward the other's face.

The striped cat's stance made any counter attack difficult, but the younger cat used his greater weight, thrusting himself forward to knock the other cat off balance. The advantage then was his, but he lacked the experience to use it, and seconds later was again in retreat with fresh claw marks on his shoulder and across the crown of his head.

Again he leaped in, only to retreat once more,

this time with blood streaming from an ear. Both cats paused, then, yowling challenges and spitting their anger. The young cat could have retreated without further injury, but he chose instead to renew his assault.

He found the older cat's jaw with one flying forepaw, and slashed through flesh that quivered with pain before the striped cat's teeth snapped shut against the young tom's toes. In a single, grinding motion, the old cat threw his head up like a dog, and his ivory teeth ripped through flesh and sinew and the pads of the young cat's foot.

Flung off balance by the move, the young tom rolled quickly upright. Barely able to use his damaged forepaw, he still snarled his defiance. But when the older cat reared up again, preparing to spring, discretion took over and the young tom turned and fled with yowls of fear. He came within a hair's breadth of having further injury even in retreat. The striped cat's teeth met in the fur of his rump, but didn't cut through the skin beneath.

The enticing female, who had circled about the fighters like a spectator at an arena, gave the younger male only a single parting glance before rolling herself on the ground before the old striped tom and mouthed noises of pleasure as she performed before him.

It was a short performance. The old cat, wise in the ways of alluring females, immediately flung her face down on the ground, then grasped her ruff with his still-bloody teeth and mounted her. Only after the vibrant emotions of his battle were spent did he allow her to renew her wanton approaches.

When the two finally wandered away from the battleground, the young tomcat followed. He kept at a discreet distance, but even so he became the subject of several fierce mock attacks by the seasoned old cat. However, as long as he kept his distance, the attacks were no threat.

The older cat mated several times with the female before his passions were spent, but after the first day and night had passed, he left her without a backward glance. And since she was still in season, she again encouraged the younger male's advances. The end result, although neither of the males knew it or would have cared, was a litter with a single dun-colored female, who accompanied the four striped and gray kittens in their immediate search for milk.

When the mating urge had passed, the gray female drove off the second of her suitors in a flurry of screaming, scratching attacks that put a speedy end to his plaintive approaches. It left the tomcat slightly confused, but there were other considerations...like hunger. After several days on meager rations, he quickly forgot about the female and began a systematic reconnaissance of the unfamiliar territory in which he was travelling.

The fruition of his full maturity had brought to the surface his natural instincts for roaming, and during the next month he prowled the reservoir area thoroughly, until one chilly morning he found himself on the high bank of the Cotter Dam itself, staring down to where a curtain of water spread into a shimmering pool before rushing over a small embankment to become the lower river. He stood, sniffing at the air, suddenly aware that it was rank with human scent.

At first he felt repelled, but he dimly remembered the scavenging days at Vanity Crossing, and finally he drifted like a gray shadow until he reached the footbridge that crossed the river below the dam.

THIRTEEN

The young cat prospered in the Cotter Reserve. He had sufficient size and strength to hold his own as a scavenger, and when the pickings were lean he knew enough about the native bush surrounding the reserve to keep himself alive without much difficulty.

As well, there were plenty of other scavengers about to serve as his prey. He caught many of the semi-tame kookaburras and crows that frequented the main camping areas. Small native marsupials were available in abundance, and there were numerous reptiles and nesting birds in the well-watered region bounded by the Cotter, Paddy's River and the great Murrumbidgee into which the Cotter flowed.

He learned to tip over the rubbish bins, and to prowl the areas near the barbecues for tasty meals of discarded chicken bones and chop morsels and other goodies left behind by the hordes of human visitors.

There were many other cats, also, since this was among the main problem areas when it came to people dumping unwanted household pets. Most of the kittens died early from starvation, from attacks by the large tomcats that roamed the area, or were caught in the traps set by rangers trying vainly to keep the feral animal problem under control.

They used live traps, baited especially for cats; traps that allowed the captured animals to be humanely dispatched after capture. The traps also allowed release of native animals, such as possums and sugar-gliders, when they were caught in the cage-like structures.

The young tom's early experience linking human-smell with his mother's death kept him more cautious than many of the other feline residents, and a lucky observation during the middle of a warm, moonlit night provided the other safety factor. He was trailing a female, a young black female approaching her first mating cycle, when the smell of bait drew his attention and brought him circling to reach it at the same time as the she-cat, who had also picked up the scent.

The tom moved quickly through the bright underbrush, but he arrived at the scene to see the she-cat twist in sudden fear and panic as the cage-trap snapped shut around her. More curious than hungry, the young male kept to the shadows, circling cautiously as he watched the female's panic-stricken contortions within the trap. She screamed in anger, clawing at the mesh of the cage until she had ripped away one claw from her forepaw. She hissed and spat when the tom's scent came to her on the breeze, somehow associating him with the cage that held her unharmed but unable to escape.

He found it all very interesting, and although he left the area periodically through that night to hunt, he kept returning to check on the female's strange antics. With the arrival of dawn he found a concealed hideout where he could watch without being seen, and when the rangers came to collect their trap later in the morning, the young tom was watching—and he had learned.

Several times in the weeks that followed, though tempted by the tantalizing smell of their baits, he never approached closely enough to be caught as he had seen the black female caught.

The young tom had no need of the bait in the traps to live well. A confident, professional hunter, able to handle any prey he sought, he generally traveled and stalked by night, when the humans in the area were asleep in tents or caravans, their abhorrent dogs tied up.

His hunting grounds were shared by a pair of young foxes, and these the tomcat avoided whenever he could. His memory still kept a special slot for fox scent, and although he was able, had he known it, to deal with either fox easily, he couldn't shake off his innate caution.

He still killed frogs and insects and small lizards, but his major hunting skills were reserved for the larger prey, the possums, gliders and bush rats that abounded in the area. And, of course, the birds. He could climb as well as any native marsupial, and his keen nose and ears allowed him to move through the jungles of underbrush on the darkest of nights, plucking low-roosting birds from their perches as if they were pieces of fruit.

Avoiding humans, he was seen by few people during his first six months on the reserve. But he saw the people who did not notice him. He saw them strewing the creek banks with beer cans. He saw them throw cigarette packets and food containers everywhere, ignoring litter bins. He saw them chop away at young trees when the forest was strewn with dead timber ideal for their illegal fires, and he watched young men carve their initials into the trunks of huge gum trees older than they were.

Often, he stalked the fishermen who moved up Paddy's River in the early dawn hours or close on dark, whipping their fly lines across the water as they sought the introduced rainbow trout, the wilier browns and the small, schooling native perch.

One evening he watched as several young men strung a net across a narrow stretch of the river, then moved in a splashing line to drive trout into it. They knew it was illegal but the cat did not. He knew only that he enjoyed the very small trout they discarded as not worth keeping.

From a lair high on a brush-strewn bank of

the Cotter, he watched a pair of cormorants fishing one night, fascinated by their graceful, sinuous movements as they dived and surfaced and dived again in their own struggle for survival. The old Powerful Owl didn't hunt far enough down to reach the reserve, but his many smaller cousins, all equally efficient at their own levels of hunting, cruised the nights on silent, stealthy wings.

Often the cat's own hunting was disturbed by the haunting cry of the Boobook Owl, who sounded his own name in an attempt to frighten small mammals into stirring enough to reveal their presence. The cat once caught and killed, with some difficulty, a barn owl that swooshed down onto a marsupial mouse almost in front of the cat's nose.

He found the flesh of the owl stringy and tough, and there was surprisingly little bird beneath the shroud of fluffy feathers.

Hunting by night as he did, the cat quite often found himself faced with the various snakes of the region. The smaller species, like the white-lipped snake and the Masters snake, despite their venom, he usually killed and ate. They were small enough to be susceptible to his peculiar form of attack, the stealthy stalk followed by a leap that placed his powerful fangs squarely behind the snake's head.

But the well-watered areas in the Cotter and Murrumbidgee drainage held large snakes as well, snakes quite capable of killing the cat should he allow himself an instant of carelessness. Usually he avoided the common red-bellied black snakes he encountered, and they were happy to avoid him in return, sliding quickly into the always-handy waters of river or creek.

The dark brown tiger snakes, with their curiously flattened heads and indistinct bands, weren't quite so shy, but they avoided confrontation with any animal as large as the cat—provided they were left alone. Since he was seldom hungry enough to deliberately bother them, the armed truce held good as a general rule.

Even with his remarkable speed and reflexes, the cat needed every stroke of luck on the rare occasion that he chose to attack a snake, especially the day he encountered a female brown snake.

He would have left her alone, after a suitable inspection to satisfy his curiosity, but this female had only recently laid her eggs, and she was in an aggressive mood. As the cat approached, stepping in on tiptoe to inspect the coiled reptile at closer range, she shrank back into her defense coil.

As she reared to face him, he could see her cream-colored belly with its spots of pink, twined in amongst the coils of her dark brown back. Had he been hungry, the cat would still have hesitated to attack this huge snake; without hunger it was only his curiosity that forced him to reach out one forepaw, as if to deliberately tease her.

The snake's head wavered as she gathered herself to strike, and when she moved the cat was prepared for it, leaping high and to one side and easily avoiding the quickness of her attack. But he had expected her to stop and recoil, and when she turned instead and drove herself along the ground to reach him, the cat had to leap again to avoid her. She didn't stop, but slithered along the ground in a series of incredibly swift undulations. The cat leaped away again, and yet again, and finally he turned and fled, instinct and plain good sense giving him the incentive to flee the snake's wrath before she touched him with her deadly fangs.

He found the experience slightly unnerving, and during the next few days he avoided all snakes with conscious thought. The female brown, successful in driving the cat away from her clutch of twenty-three eggs in their shallow burrow beneath a fallen log, didn't chase him very far. The cat was too large to serve her as prey, although she had taken her share of small kittens when the opportunity arose.

Her attack on the cat was worthy of a maternal attitude, but the snake soon abandoned the eggs, which were found later by an alert kookaburra who smashed all that he didn't eat. Other small predators cleaned up the rest.

FOURTEEN

The first weekend of spring saw the Cotter Reserve transformed. Even before noon on Saturday, bright orange and blue tents and shiny camper trailers began popping up like mushrooms upon the grassy open spaces beneath the large trees in the camping section. Tendrils of smoke were thin gray signals from the fireplaces and barbecues in the reserve, and the air was alive with the sounds of screaming, laughing children and the incessant yapping of dozens of dogs.

"Like a blooming circus, isn't it?" Dave Bates said, as he leaned against the side of Jack Fielding's truck and surveyed the throng with a distinctly unimpressed eye. Over the din of the children and dogs could be heard the occasional blare of a transistor radio, and from one caravan the noise declared that its owner had brought his television along.

"I don't for the life of me know how you ranger blokes put up with it," Dave told Jack. "Any of these people would find more peace and quiet in their own back yard than out here. And look at the silly galahs. Most of them bring along everything they'd already have if they stayed home. Go to the bush where there's peace and quiet, except for the other forty thousand fools who get there before you." He spat disgustedly.

"They have to have someplace to go," Jack replied. "And better to have them concentrated here than wandering all over the place. At least this way we can keep an eye on them."

The two men watched with ill-concealed incredulity and repugnance as a man old enough to know better tossed an empty stubby toward a trash bin without even looking to see if it landed inside.

Jack tensed as the bottle smashed on the rim of the metal trash can, but when the man didn't even look around, he sighed heavily and relaxed. "No sense," he muttered. "One day the whole world is going to drown in its own garbage, I reckon."

Even as they watched, rubbish was thrown at the tins by various people, most of them with questionable accuracy. But three times as many did not even attempt to use the rubbish bins, and equally ignored Jack in his ranger uniform.

"See what I mean?" he said, after a bit. "And there's no sense even talking to most of them about it. Last time I had words with a bloke about spreading his rubbish around, he just pointed to all the rest of it and laughed in my face. That's the one really good thing about these reserves. It keeps all the silly cows in one place, which I guess is better than having them scattered all over the bush. At least here we can keep an eye on them without having to worry too much about them getting lost or setting half the country on fire. But it'll happen one day, a fire I mean, you wait and see."

"I've already seen," Dave said. "Saw a fellow the other day lighting a fire, not five feet from a sign telling him he couldn't. There wasn't a chance in hell he could have missed seeing that bloody sign. What surprised me was that he didn't knock it off and use it for kindling."

They watched the passing parade for a few more minutes before Jack mentioned the cat.

"You mean he's down here now?" Dave said with a look of total surprise. "You've seen him, yourself?"

"Yeah. I'm pretty sure it was him. Big, rangy fellow. Looks like a Siamese except he's striped underneath, and where a Siamese is dark he's sort of got patterns...more stripes, I guess."

"Must be him, mate. I wouldn't have thought he'd wander this far, especially with so many people about. But it must be him. There wouldn't be that many Siamese-type cats running around the country. And maybe he got used to scrounging back at Vanity Crossing."

"He's the only Siamese I've ever seen down here," said Jack. "And we've never picked one up in the traps. I guess people who pay good money for their cats take better care of them, don't chuck them in the bush first time one gets herself pregnant."

He paused to light his pipe before continuing. "Anyway, if this cat is Toby's son, he's just about king of the castle 'round here. Monstrous beast, he is. Must weight eighteen or nineteen pounds. One of the other fellows saw him fighting with a big old brindle tomcat one morning, and he said it was the fastest, roughest fight he's ever seen. I'm pretty sure it was him that clawed half the hide off a yappy little poodle that was pawing in the garbage cans the other night. I didn't actually see it happen, but I wish I had. The stupid poodle, not on a leash like he was supposed to be, of course, made a real nuisance of himself around the place all day. And just on dusk, up near the dam, there was the greatest racket you ever heard. Two minutes later this poor dog came flying out of the scrub with claw marks all over him. Looked as if he'd been caught up in a barbed-wire fence."

"Must have made his owner happy," Dave said. "Or did he even have one?"

"Oh, my very word he did, and the man was just ropeable. He came over and started giving me all kinds of rubbish about wild animals, and then got stroppy when I told him to read the signs and keep his dog on a leash like he's supposed to."

Jack laughed harshly. "Said he was going to report me to the Minister, that's what he said.

And the Prime Minister, if he didn't get proper respect. I told him not to forget the Queen, and then I left. Reckon his dog had more brains, and it was pretty stupid."

"Not hard to tell who's smartest," Dave said with a chuckle. "The way most people train their dogs, it's usually the people who end up trained. They always forget the first rule of dog training. You've got to be smarter than the dog."

Jack Fielding bellowed in honest laughter at that, but he sobered quickly at the sight of a pack of assorted dogs that bounded suddenly from the underbrush beside the creek. There were seven, in all, including three that looked to be pure-bred animals. One was an Irish Setter, his red fur dripping and matted and hung with burrs, while another was a young, gangling German Shorthaired Pointer. The leader of the impromptu pack was a huge kelpie whose dingo blood showed up in its pale yellow coat and the splashes of white at his ankles.

"There'd be a sheep-killer or two in that bunch if you put them in the right place," Dave said.

"The kelpie, I reckon." Jack scowled. "He's been around here the last couple of weeks, off and on, and I've never seen anybody with him. I think he's a stray, but we can't manage to get him into a trap. He's really spooky."

"Well it's no wonder there are more and more graziers in the district who'll shoot any stray as soon as look at him. You hear some pretty ghastly stories from those with properties close to the city."

"Too right! And you can't blame the graziers, either. People who really care for their dogs keep them under control. Once they start running wild they're good for nothing anyway. Probably better if they're shot than if they kill stock or attack somebody's kiddies. It'll happen to some politician's kid one day, and that's when you'll hear the screams for better dog control."

"It'll never happen," Dave said soberly. "People worry more about what happens to dogs than they do about other people, I think. Maybe rightly so. I prefer a good dog myself. But they'll let them run loose, then cry when they die of tick poisoning or dingo bait. Should you try and institute proper controls, they'd be after your scalp. Look what happened to that grazier who shot somebody's pure-bred Doberman out near Hall last year. He got threatened with lawsuits, and he's suffered all kinds of vandalism ever since. Or at least the police keep saying it's vandalism. Funny his place is the only one that seems to cop it, though.'

"Especially when he'd already lost half a dozen sheep to town dogs, and likely the Doberman was one of them."

"He'd lose just as many to that kelpie," said Dave, gesturing with his pipe.

He and Jack watched the pack make another swing through the reserve, one of them leaving the formation only long enough snatch a half-eaten hot-dog from a child's fingers. Jack shouted at the dogs, but he might as well have bayed at the moon. Wherever their owners were, it was clear that nobody planned to control the animals until it came time to pack up and go home for tea.

"That's pretty rough, Jack. Can't you do anything at all about it?" Dave's tone of voice hinted he already knew the answer.

"Mate, we've barely got enough people to handle our routine patrols. We get the occasional dog, of course, but when it's this crowded, all we can do is advise the owners of the rules...then watch them ignore us. If it was left to me, I reckon I'd arrange some kind of great big kennel on the edge of the reserve and insist that people put their dogs in it before they even get out of their cars. But I know it's not very realistic."

"Damn, there ought to be some kind of order," Dave said with another scowl. "What about those people who don't have dogs? Aren't they entitled to some rights too?"

"Sure they are. But the rules aren't rigid enough, and they're too hard to enforce. It would take an army of rangers to achieve proper dog control without the legislation that would allow us to force people to control their pets. Maybe someday..."

FIFTEEN

They came out of the underbrush like a pack of ravening wolves, running silently behind the self-appointed leader, the huge, gaunt kelpie with his beer-bottle eyes. Only four of the dogs remained from the pack seen by Dave and Jack during the afternoon; the great, dingo-like kelpie, a second dog that was nearly as large and looked to be a Labrador-Alsatian cross-breed, and two smaller dogs that could have been any breed at all, and looked it. The three pure-bred dogs were gone, finally called in after considerable effort on the part of their owners. Their removal had taken the tongue from the pack.

The cat, of course, had been mildly aware of the dogs throughout the day. Earlier, their racket had wakened him from his snug nest beneath a bramble thicket along Paddy's River, but he hadn't been overly concerned because they'd confined their ramblings to the more populated sections of the reserve. It had been a group of children, rather than the dogs, which had finally forced the cat to leave his bed and wander up into the pine forest along the Tidbinbilla Road.

With the coming of twilight, he'd crossed the road and moved onto the open hillside where the small mice and birds tended to feed in the early evening. He was stalking one especially rotund little mouse when the pack surged into the open behind him, the kelpie snuffling now and then to hold the scent left by the meandering cat.

The cat heard the snuffling as the pack broke into the open, and as the kelpie lifted his head to expose broad, shining fangs and the big crossbreed yelped with excitement, the cat was already standing tall to get a proper view of them and wondering in his feline mind what action to take. They gave him little enough time. Even as the cat turned to survey his possible escape routes, the kelpie uttered a booming growl that was taken up by the others in a chorus of barks and yelps.

If the kelpie had been alone, the cat might have fought him. The cat had frightened off more than one dog that size during his adulthood. But he knew he couldn't handle four of them, and as they began to give chase he turned and streaked away through the tall grass, heading for the only trees he could see. Cut off from above, he was forced down the ridge, and the trees were a long way off.

The dogs followed, baying joyously. They weren't really hungry, and except for the kelpie they weren't even especially strong cat-haters. But they were born hunters, each of them, and the sight of a prey which would run removed the last vestige of training or caution. They swung after the cat in a body, low to the ground as their legs churned, seeking more speed. Tongues hanging from desperate, gasping jowls, they barked or howled according to their breeds, though after his initial growl the kelpie was as silent as death itself.

The cat knew fear. Though he was well-rested and the pack had been running all day, there was little question that they would catch him in time. No cat has the endurance to run at top speed for long.

Even the cheetah, noted speedster of the African plains and considered one of the fastest animals in the world, is specifically designed for the long stalk and the short chase, using his initial burst of incredible speed to catch his prey before it can build up sufficient speed to get away. Once past that initial impetus, a cat's heart and lungs demand a return to a slower pace, a sort of trot that would have nowhere near the speed needed by the young tomcat.

Because it was downhill at the beginning, he had less trouble than he expected, but at the bottom of the ridge was the bitumen road, and the only available trees were across it or far to the cat's right. There wasn't much choice, really, and the cat didn't pause to consider. Pain from his tortured lungs built to an uncontrollable level, and his eyes were blinded by the pressure of blood soaring through his heaving muscles. He turned on the bottom of the shallow ditch and heaved himself to the roadway, oblivious to everything but trees ahead and death behind.

The cars moved down the hill quickly, their drivers anxious to get home. Distracted by squalling, over-tired, sunburned children, and fractious pets, they traveled too close to each other for proper safety, and despite the failing daylight, only one driver had bothered to turn on his headlights. The cat didn't see the head-lights, and he didn't hear the screeching of brakes under full lock or the high-pitched shriek of tires smoking as the sedan slid to a halt. He was halfway across the road when the tire hit him, and the impact threw him the rest of the way.

He landed on the far side of the road ditch, only yards from the shelter of the trees, but the pain of broken ribs knifed through him as he lurched to his feet and shambled forward. He sensed, somehow, that the pursuit was over, but something inside him demanded that he keep on fleeing, until he was well away from the cacophony of yelping dogs and honking car horns and the shouts of angry people.

In fairness, although it was hardly relevant to the cat, the driver of the car that struck him didn't even see the shadowy figure as it crossed in front of his vehicle. He was busy arguing with his wife when he looked up to see the pack of dogs almost upon him, and it was the dogs he tried to avoid when he locked his brakes and slewed his car halfway across the roadway. The driver behind saw only the flash of brakelights and the flurry of the pack on his left. The third driver in line didn't see the dogs at all. The fourth saw the dogs, but not the brakelights of the third. And the fifth, sixth and seventh drivers involved in the rather spectacular chain-reaction collision had only the excuse of following too closely.

No one was injured, except in their wallets, and none of the cars were sufficiently damaged to prevent anyone from getting home that night.

Jack Fielding, who arrived shortly after the collision, and the owner of the first car spent several minutes searching for whatever the driver had struck, or thought he'd struck. "There was a little thump," he said, "but I didn't see anything but those flaming dogs."

The drivers in the other cars confirmed that they'd seen only the four dogs, and all four played and chased each other on the grass beside the roadway while the accident was sorted out. Finally, despite Jack's conviction that they must have been chasing something or they wouldn't have approached the roadway as they had, he was forced to abandon his search and straighten out the muddle of vehicles, trying to clear them off the road while everybody waited for the police to arrive.

There was considerable discussion among the angry drivers regarding people who allowed their animals to run loose and cause accidents, and what should be done about it. But each driver also knew that even the dogs would provide little justification when they faced their insurance companies, or the courts. Only one driver of the seven, as it turned out, had imbibed sufficiently during his day's outing to interest the police when they arrived.

The net result was something like $15,000 in damages and a series of vague threats about lawsuits against the owners of the dogs should they ever be identified. And although none of this provided any consolation to the injured cat, who was two miles away by then, it was of some satisfaction to Jack Fielding, who knew old Dave Bates would be equally amused when told about it.

SIXTEEN

The cat was in agony.

Each movement, however slight, drove slivers of pain through his body, and every time he took a step with his right forefoot, he could feel the corresponding shifting of the cracked and broken ribs on that side. But he could not, would not stop. Instinct had taken over from his conscious mind, and instinct drove him to keep moving... moving, despite the thin blood trail from the missing patch of hide on his right side; moving, despite the pain that had nearly brought him to unconsciousness several times since the accident.

Instinct forced him back through the tangled

underbrush along Paddy's River, then across the dreaded bitumen and up into the pine forest, far from the dogs and the people and the rank proliferation of smells that meant danger. When he reached the ridge above the road, deep in the cool depth of the pine forest, he paused only briefly to stare through pain-dulled eyes at the slope ahead. Once again, instinct forced him upward and onward, over the ridges and down to the shelter of the native underbrush along the Cotter. He shambled down through the timber, stumbling and falling in his agony, resting for a moment after each fall, until he regained enough strength to continue. Almost blinded by pain, he unerringly headed for the one area where he could feel reasonably safe.

It took him almost the entire night to find what he sought.

Just before the hazy streaks of early dawn began to lighten the sky, he discovered an abandoned wombat burrow not far from the tinkling waters of the river. The broad opening would be difficult to defend if it came to that, but his exhausted, battered body would take him no further and he knew it. Using the remainder of his strength, he stalked quickly around the site, spraying his urine onto appropriate bushes and tree trunks in a final effort to mark the territory as his own. Then he lurched into the burrow, curled himself gently down onto the small matting of old dried grasses, and passed out.

SEVENTEEN

During the next twenty-four hours, the cat wakened only twice. Once when pain and the side effects of his shock brought him suddenly awake in a spasm of vomit and coughing, and the second time when he shuddered awake almost rigid with cold and bone-shaking chills. Each time, he fumbled blindly in his attempts to lick the still-open wound, but he found his stiffened side made it difficult to reach it properly with his healing tongue.

In the two days that followed, he awakened several times, but his pain-wracked body would not respond properly, and each time he sank quickly again into the soothing respite of unconsciousness.

The wound began to scab over, but each time he tried to twist and lick at it, the sharp pains inside him forced him to stop. Hunger came and went, and usually he slept when it was most severe, so he reacted by twitching his stiff body and mewing plaintively through a series of unremembered nightmares.

By the evening of the fourth day, hunger had become a consuming fire in his guts, and despite the pain and stiffness he knew he must find food. It took him half an hour to make it to his feet, grunting and crying with the pain and the effort of moving at all. Finally, however, he succeeded, and on shaky legs he fumbled his way up the short tunnel to the world outside. He lurched his way into the silvery beams of moonlight, where he collapsed in a trembling heap and lay for long minutes before he could summon the strength to rise again.

The remainder of the night was torture. He moved step by agonizing step, unable to stifle the occasional gasps of pain when he put a foot down wrongly. He couldn't even think about climbing a low shrub where his nose revealed a nesting bird and her eggs. He stumbled upon potential prey several other times, but always his laborious progress alerted the small brown marsupial mice and swift tree frogs before he could get within stalking distance. Thirst and fever raged through his system, and his normally magnificent senses of hearing and night-vision had all but deserted him. Pure luck, after several hours, brought him to a marsupial mouse who was less alert than the others, but then it deserted him again and the tiny mouse was off and running before the cat could grab it.

Sensing his presence, the marsupial slithered under some fallen timber to the relative safety of its nest, and the cat followed by smell alone. The mouse was too quick, but its seven tiny babies had no such advantage. Seven tiny morsels, each of them not even a full mouthful for the ravenous cat. But he ate them gratefully, slowly, devouring each tiny nibble and feeling his body respond to the warmth of the food.

Then the thirst came again, this time so fierce he could not ignore it. Half an hour to shuffle and scramble his way the few hundred yards to the river, and then the agony of descent and the distasteful situation of having to wade in almost to his shoulders to drink. He couldn't crouch properly without shafts of pain spearing through him from the broken ribs. The water itself was cool, almost frigid, but he found that it had a balming effect on his wound as it lapped against him, and he stepped forward, without thinking, to let the coolness bathe him and still the continuous, throbbing pain.

As the soreness abated, it was replaced by sheer cold, and when he could no longer stand that, he hunched himself back up the slope, carefully shook the excess water from his fur in a series of painful, tiny shudders, and returned to his underground haven. Sleep claimed him again almost immediately.

Throughout the remainder of the night he shivered and twitched, unable to get comfortable because of the chilling dampness of his fur. With the rising sun, he dragged himself out once again to the surface, where he spent the entire day lying in the warming rays of the sun. But the coming of the next night brought fresh pangs of hunger, and again he was forced into the ordeal of hunting. The nest of a small, ground-nesting bird brought some nourishment; the hen fled, but he gulped down her eggs with scant regard for the tacky bits of shell that adhered to his whiskers.

Sheer bluff became his major ally later that night, when a large native cat killed a bush rat almost in his path. The native slayer had barely begun to savor his meal when the tomcat stumbled around the corner of the track and slumped into what was supposed to be a threatening crouch. His injured side forced out a moan of pain that mingled with his hissing snarl of defiance at the native cat.

The native cat shifted to its own defensive posture and faced the much larger intruder. The tomcat's fur rose in a massive ruff around his neck, and his tail lashed faster and faster as he stealthily moved forward, jaws chopping and saliva dripping from his famished mouth.

At first, it appeared the spotted native cat would defend his prey; had he simply grabbed it and run he would have been safe enough. But as the big tomcat approached, the smaller native cat moved back pace by pace, and when the tomcat lurched forward to land on the dead rat with a painful cry of triumph, the native cat took discretion to heart and fled the scene.

Some time later, the cat left the scant remains and again aimed for the river and the water his system demanded. When he'd drunk, he lay down in the shallow water and let the current bathe his injured side.

By the end of the week, the cat had been reduced to little more than a walking skeleton. His hunting forays were longer and more arduous, but seldom very successful. Without the fortuitous circumstance of the bush rat, he would have died, since only the occasional egg and slow, stupid frog fell to his weakening attacks.

He was forced to spend all of each night and part of each day in hunting, sleeping away the rest of the warmer daylight hours in the sunshine as he stretched his painful muscles and gradually exercised the wounded side. Eventually, he could reach over his shoulder to lick at the healing scab, and the flesh knitted fairly well. But although the cracked ribs from the accident had also begun to knit well, the two lowest ones, smashed severely, refused to come together properly. This was aggravated by his necessary movements while hunting, and at no time could he move without some pain.

His strength was reduced by lack of food, and his eyes were constantly dulled by pain and slow starvation. The more alert animals easily avoided his clumsy stalking, and his rushes of attack were slow and equally clumsy. What he could catch didn't provide him sufficient nourishment, but it did keep him alive. Barely.

Climbing was impossible, despite the allure of several nesting birds within easy walking distance of the lair he used, but other game, game he *could* catch, became more difficult to find each day, unless he spent long periods traveling afield.

The morning he ran across the young echidna, he was almost too weak to consider attacking it, and his first forays against the quill-protected monotreme were fruitless. The echidna simply tucked in its head and paws at the cat's approach and presented him with an impenetrable forest of sharp-pointed quills. Had it been old enough to dig itself into the earth more quickly, it would have escaped. But the cat, by accident as much as anything else, got one paw underneath the creature and flipped it onto its back.

What happened next was no accident. Before the echidna could think of righting itself to regain the protection of its spines, the big cat took it by the throat and ripped it down the belly with a single slash of his forepaw. A second later he was happily gorging himself, his entire body rejoicing at the abundance of fresh, nourishing meat. He ate every morsel his shrunken belly would take, then lay up beside the kill and rested until he could eat again.

The next night, his strength replenished to some degree, he was able to ambush an unwary bush rat, and although his ribs suffered in the tussle that ensued, the rich, hot meat was more than compensation. When the rat had been eaten, he chanced upon three separate mouse nests, complete with small morsels of necessary tucker. And then he found a young possum, wounded in an earlier encounter with an owl.

Slowly, then, his own recovery began to take place, his strength returning as he grew more capable of trapping enough proper food to satisfy the needs of his large frame. The wound on his side had healed nicely, the cracked ribs no longer troubled him, but the broken ones would not knit, and his balance, walk and leaping ability suffered as a result. Every move had to be carefully planned and performed, or spasms of pain would shoot through his chest area and belly. He tried once to climb, but he could not. And any clumsy step was likely to throw him so far off balance that he would have difficulty making the next.

But still his general condition improved, and he adapted his hunting skills and gradually learned to adjust to the weakness of the broken ribs, though he was far from his former peak condition.

Aware of his relative weakness, he maintained the abandoned wombat bureau as his lair. He kept to its dry, warm protection against the weather, and most days found him baking in the sun at the entrance for a portion of the time. He began to regain weight rapidly, but he feared his clumsiness, and because he didn't feel totally fit, he held to the safety of the lair instead of resuming his wanderings.

There were no other cats living in the area, and the single time during his recovery period that he crossed the path of another tomcat, wandering through the territory, he sniffed at it and turned away, knowing he was in no shape for any sort of battle. Had there been a receptive female involved, he might have thought twice, but without that incentive he was content to avoid all possible trouble.

Because of his injury, he was restricted to ground-level hunting, which made it all the more difficult to ensure a substantial diet level. There was plenty of food above him, birds in their nests and on their perches at night, possums and gliders high in the trees, but he couldn't reach them and his injured ribs prevented him from trying. So his diet included more mice and small lizards and frogs. As he grew accustomed to coping with his lame side, his luck improved, along with his skills.

The relatively lazy life suited him. Though lonely, he felt well rested and generally content.

EIGHTEEN

The rain began as a weather system far out in the Great Australian Bight, and gradually moved in dense masses of cloud until it struck the higher peaks of the Snowy Mountains. Then, for some reason, it slowed in its north-eastern cycle, and the clouds hovered like dark, wind-skirled shadows above the peaks. High winds brought more moist air, and the clouds began to shatter at the bottom, releasing the rain at first in small drops and then in larger ones. The winds picked up, driving small boats before it until none dared remain on the frothy waters of Lake Eucumbene. The levels began to rise in the Tantangara Reservoir, and then the first of the clouds began to move into the head-waters of the Cotter, at the far southern edge of the Australian Capital Territory.

Within a day, the slopes leading west down Mount Murray were sopping, and each tiny, usually-dry spring on the side of the range was primed by the slow, steady rain, adding even more water to the trickling rivulets. The rain system didn't move a great deal; it was sunny and fine in Canberra and on the lower reaches of the Cotter. Only the great Mother Murrumbidgee, taking nourishment from the wide-spread feeder streams near Tantangara Reservoir and growing as it flowed first southward toward Cooma and then back on itself to the north again, showed signs of the heavy local rains in the southwest.

As the Murrumbidgee grew sullen and dark with suspended silt, the Cotter River also began to show signs of swelling. First the high Corin Dam took what it could from the rains, and when it was full the water poured on down-stream as if chased by the dripping clouds, until the Bendora Dam was filled to overflowing. But still it was fine in Canberra.

Those whose job it is to know about such

things had the figures. Almost at the instant that the brown, frothing waters of the Murrumbidgee began to claw away the approaches to Angle Crossing, south of Canberra, the smaller but equally ferocious waters of the little Cotter River spilled over the crest of Bendora Dam and began to fight a path down the narrow gorge below. And the high black skirts of the rain system lifted to let the rain follow, dumping water into the turbulent stream almost as quickly as what was added from the overflowing dam. The clouds moved like a huge black wraith, and the water surged and leaped through the valley, picking up driftwood from previous floods, overturning huge rocks and gouging into the banks on every curve.

The trout were first to notice the dangers, and they quickly began to fight their way into the high narrows of the small feeder streams or downstream into the safety of the Cotter Reservoir. Some of the smaller creatures downstream, still with the sun upon them despite the approaching storm, also felt the warning in the fateful vibrations of the air and ground around them, and began moving up, away from the destruction that was cutting through the valley to the bones of the bedrock below.

The wall of water that smashed around the corner and across Vanity Crossing took with it much of the gravel that usually banked the approaches to the concreted ford. Swinging past the lower corner just downstream from the crossing, the waters flung dead trees and tangles of spiky blackberry into the whirlpools and smashed a shortcut through the edge of the corner, washing gravel and trees and small shrubbery with equal violence.

The water smashed and churned its way downstream, surging far up into the smaller channel of Condor Creek and then turning again to the east to bash through tangles of blackberry and the steep, rocky slopes of the narrow valley beyond. Ahead of the water, now, the wind-tattered clouds thrust a curtain of raindrops through the valley, and it was the rain that was the cat's undoing. Caught far from his lair, which was already under water in any event, he sought shelter beneath a blackberry thicket. His senses were suspicious of the unseen, unknown dangers of the coming flood, but his dislike of the rain overshadowed his faint urges to move up to higher ground. By the time he did move, it was too late.

His shambling, unsteady gait wasn't quick enough, and he couldn't muster the strength for a direct assault on the steep hillside above him. So he moved downstream, climbing gradually but very slowly over the soggy, treacherous ground.

Faced by a narrow, rain-slicked gully, he was forced to take a dropping trail to cross it, and the rushing wall of the floodwaters caught him halfway across. The water flashed into the foot of the gully, then stretched out an amoebic arm and snatched the cat from his precarious track. It was a flickering, almost gentle gesture, but it was enough to knock the unsteady beast from his feet, and a moment later he was struggling mightily in the muscular grip of the main flood current.

Over and over he tumbled, oblivious now to his wound or the pain in his ribs that shot bolts of agony through his thrashing body. He broke again and again to the surface, only to be thrust down as soon as he had gained a breath. Then one of his feet caught in something vaguely solid, and he twisted frantically to further his grip on the dense tangle of blackberry bushes, turned up by the roots when the floodwater struck them. The bushes floated high, and the cat somehow managed to clamber through them until his head was clear of the frothing, muddy water.

But only for a moment. Then the cat and the twisted thorn bush tumbled together, over and over again until they surfaced once more and the half-drowned cat could gasp in another breath.

There was a sudden jerk, and for an instant all the pressures of the river left him, only to return again more strongly than ever. The tangle of blackberry had jammed itself into the low-spread branches of a fallen river gum, and even as the cat struggled to free himself, the water forced the tangled blackberry bush further into place.

With only his head and one forepaw clear of the still-rising water, the cat lay panting as he fought to regain his breath, to muster sufficient strength to clamber higher into the tangled thorns of the blackberry. Beneath him, water-driven branches and small logs did their best to dislodge the thicket, and even as he scrambled a few inches higher, clearing his shoulders from the chill of the muddy water, a thick, short chunk of driftwood smashed squarely across his tender, wounded side.

He screamed at the pain of it, trying desperately to climb higher but unable to move. After several minutes, he gained another few precious inches before being struck a glancing blow from another floating branch. This one knocked him almost clear of the blackberry tangle, almost back into the grasping arms of the river.

Little by little, however, he managed to struggle further upward, forcing himself into the blackberry thicket and ignoring the needles of thorns that tore at his side and slashed across his face. It was as if he had snared himself in a bale of barbed wire fencing; every little bit he crawled seemed to bring him more and more thoroughly into a smothering cage of thorns. But he feared the water more, and as the flood crest passed he raised himself until only one limp hind leg was still being tugged by the current.

Then a huge branch, smashed from an upstream gum by the driving wind, ground into his refuge. The bottom of it tucked into the blackberries, but the top swung with the current and smashed across the cat's face, knocking him unconscious.

NINETEEN

It was hours before the cat came to, hours in which the peak of the flood passed to oblivion inside the reservoir of the Cotter Dam, leaving only a ghost of itself to tumble over the high crest and down into the lower river for the short, fast ride to the muddy, swollen Murrumbidgee. The black clouds had been whipped to shreds by the wind, the rain had ended, and the first hints of daylight were beginning to peek shyly over the sodden ridges.

The cat was well clear of the water, which had dropped nearly thirty inches. But a new cluster of blackberry had jammed in after him, and the cat was well and truly a prisoner in the razor-sharp, clinging thorns. Half-dried blood blurred the vision in one eye, and the other was swollen shut. He snorted several times to clear the mucus from his throat and nose, but could do nothing to ease the throbbing, continuing pain from the injuries to his body.

The thorns, along with the branches in the water, had torn open the wound in his side, although not nearly so bad as when it was fresh. But inside him, the still unhealed broken ribs were loose again and moving, causing him pain with every twist and gasping breath. He struggled valiantly, his own sharp claws more than matched by the hundreds of thorns that grasped at him. He writhed and twisted and slashed with the two feet that remained partially free, but in moments he was exhausted, both from his ordeal and from the panic he couldn't control.

The thorns were caught in his matted fur, in the raw red wound in his side, even in the short fur of his twitching tail. And every move that freed him from one seemed to leave him open to assault from a hundred more.

He struggled and twisted and fought and clawed his way, making agonizingly small gains throughout the morning, and when the sun reached its zenith, he seemed no further ahead than before. But he was warm, and as the sun dried his fur and poured its warmth down upon the soaked valley, the cat's exhaustion began to take its toll.

He rested, then struggled some more. Then rested again. The water dropped further below him, still sulky and dark from the mud it carried, but dropping swiftly now that the runoff wasn't filling the dams upstream. The bush no longer dripped with moisture, although the noise of the water still thundered loud in the cat's ears.

Finally, he could try no more. Exhaustion claimed him, and he surrendered to the warmth of the sun and slept in his prison-cradle of thorns.

TWENTY

Dave Bates leaned heavily on his walking staff, silently cursing at the shakiness of his legs. He had been on the move since early morning, and although he was aware of the extra strain imposed by the rain-slicked walking conditions, he did not like admitting how much it affected him. As he stood immobile, scouring the flooded valley with his gaze, the muscles of his calves and thighs quivered from the pressure of the work they had done that day.

"Must be getting old," he muttered half aloud. "Damned foolishness anyway, this trudging around in the mud."

He fiddled idly with the straps of his rucksack and wondered what inner devil had created his fascination with the working of floods. He had seen them in the dry washes of the outback, where monstrous walls of water smashed like liquid cement along gullies that had been dry for years, and he had seen them in the overgrown, jungly rivers of the coastal fringe, where at least two floods a year was the rule instead of the exception. And always he was enthralled by the harshness and violence of nature at work, the damage and change and new life which a flood could create.

Rather than hike in from the face of the Cotter Dam, where he knew the breadth of the reservoir would have taken up and absorbed the shock of the flood, he had driven into the Pierce's Creek forestry depot and walked west to the river from there. It had been a highly educational journey.

Tiny Pierce's Creek, never much of a waterway at the best of times, had missed most of the rain along its short route, and showed no signs of flooding except where it dipped to unite with the larger Cotter River. There, the driving force of the flood had scoured out fresh channels at the junction of the two streams, and had obviously backed up the waters of the small creek for several hundred yards.

Even though the crest of the flood was long past, Dave could travel only well above the natural high water mark, and he could see that it would be days or even weeks before the Cotter returned to it normal clarity. The rains had primed every tiny spring and small rivulet in the hills surrounding the river, and each had contributed a share to the murky siltation that had turned the river the color of mud.

As he moved downstream, treading lightly and with care over silt-slicked boulders and trying to avoid the free-flowing springs in the hillside, he could see where the flood had smashed its way over low points between several sharp bends, forcing out entirely new channels in several places. At one curve, the old channel was already showing that it would end up being dried out entirely. A huge old log had somehow become wedged across it, and the subsequent piling of debris and gravel had forced the river to turn aside and slash itself a new track over the neck of land that had created the original curve.

High on the banks, where the water had

swirled a good metre above its present level, tangles of driftwood were jammed into crutches of trees, huge bushes were virtually flattened by the power of the river, and sections of the hill-side itself were scoured to become new scars where the water had probed efficiently for any weakness in the union of rock and dirt and root-let.

The old man moved carefully along the pre-carious hillsides, ever conscious of the dangers a misstep could bring. Once, many years before, blatant carelessness had left him to crawl and flounder his way, with a broken ankle, down eleven miles of rocky, twisted creek bed. It had been entirely his own fault, and while the risk of a similar accident was a constant companion to any lone bush-walker, Dave knew that care could keep the risk to a minimum.

He paused often in his tour of the river. Moving caused him to concentrate too much on his footing, and he couldn't observe the area around him. In order to see what he'd come to see, he had to halt and deliberately survey the terrain. His old eyes were still sharp, and over the years he'd become trained through practice in the art of *seeing* as it applied to the bush. It is seldom the direct act of looking that shows the bushwalker the life and movement around him, but the peripheral vision, the indirect, often unrealized clarity that comes from the edges of the line of sight.

Many animals, and sometimes man himself, in times of stress, can unconsciously feel a direct gaze, even though the seer may not be aware of what he is looking at. But once the directness of the gaze has passed, a tiny flicker of motion, an unnoticed shape or color will at times bring out an object that the direct glance hasn't recognized. Dave Bates had actually passed the fallen tree with its heavy burden of blackberry, and it wasn't until he'd walked several paces past it and turned up the ridge that the unconscious pinging of his mind forced him to turn and look again. And from that angle, the cat was *just* visible, a mere shadow within the tortured withes of the thorny blackberry tangle.

At first glance, he doubted what he saw, so he walked down to the water's edge and peered into the massed thornbush from several angles. Once the shape of the cat had revealed itself, however, he paused only a moment to offload his rucksack before moving cautiously into the fast-flowing, muddy water. He used the fallen tree for support, and probed with his staff before him to ensure he didn't step into some unknown, unseen hole in the rocky bottom. And as the chill water snapped at his knees with icy teeth, he cursed at the folly of it all; surely the cat couldn't still be alive.

The water was cold and riddled with treacherous undercurrents, and by the time Dave had reached the crutch of the tree, where he could actually touch the edges of the tangled blackberry thicket, he had almost been swept from his tenuous hold once and had slipped into one hole that plunged him to the waist in the chill water.

It took him twenty minutes to shift aside the spiky, whippy branches enough to reach out and touch the motionless form of the wounded cat. And another five minutes, after having muttered his surprise that the animal still breathed, to gently free the cat and begin his retreat to the shore with the animal cradled as softly as he could arrange it against his chest. Throughout the journey, the cat never moved, and Dave was only barely aware of its rasping breathing.

When he reached the relative safety of the shore, he scooped up his rucksack and laboriously climbed up, moving along the bank and higher until he reached the shelter of a small cluster of brush with a small meadow of short grass that shone bright green between large rocks. He carefully laid the cat down on the grass and fumbled into his rucksack for the gear he thought he might need.

First, he removed the green-and-silver reversible "space" blanket which he carried always. A warming shawl when required, it was waterproof, and the reflective side had proved handy many times when he huddled, wet and chilly, before a small fire. He breathed a sigh of thanks as he spread the space blanket and gently shifted the cat onto the reflective surface, where the intensified rays of the sun would provide instant warmth. Then Dave rigged a tripod of sticks to support the edges of the blanket around the cat's still figure and began assembling fire materials.

He fumbled his first attempt to get the fire started, and it was not until he had fumbled again that he realized how chilled he had become. His gnarled fingers trembled, and he dropped several of the waxed matches into the damp grass before he forced himself to move more slowly. "Easy does it, old man," he muttered. "Keep this up and you'll end up as bad off as that poor damned cat."

In a few minutes, then, he had the fire going nicely and the shiny, reflective surface of the space blanket was shimmering waves of heat over the still-unconscious animal. Dave could see the steam rising from his own soaked trousers. "Righto, that's under control," he said. "Now I wonder what it is I should try and do for a half-drowned cat." He turned and gently shifted the cat's body, noting with sensitive fingers the swelling of the wrongly-healed lower ribs, the bloody wound on the animal's side, and the obvious facial injuries. The cat's breathing was harsh, faltering, and seemed to the old man to be blocked by mucus. Periodically the cat uttered a low, rasping cough, but he showed no sign of regaining consciousness.

Dave peeled back one eyelid, noting the dry, feverish look of the exposed eye, then gently prized open the cat's mouth to ensure there was nothing inside to block its breathing. The obvious injuries were worrying, but it was the damage to the cat's ribs that bothered Dave the most. He was no proper veterinarian, but he'd had a lifetime of dealing with animals, and he could see that the rib damage was the worst problem.

As he cautiously shifted the cat's body around, probing very lightly to discover how much damage there really was, the cat uttered several painful, grunting sounds, but still wouldn't waken. And there seemed to be a pink froth gathering around the corners of his mouth. Dave shook his head at the sight of that; it meant the strong likelihood of a punctured or lacerated lung or else definite internal injuries.

"Well, old mate. I wonder if you've got any chance at all," he whispered. "I reckon you might be better off if I put your out of your misery now, while you're asleep. There's no way you'll be able to fend for yourself with those injuries, and I can't see you lasting the distance if I was to try and carry you out of here and find a vet."

He looked for some sign that the cat could hear him, was aware of his presence, but there was none. "I don't reckon you'd like being kept," he continued. "It'd mean being caged, good tucker every day, but no more roaming wild in the bush. You'd probably die anyway."

He continued muttering to himself and the cat for several minutes, half convinced he should end the animal's suffering immediately, but not quite able to bring himself to do it. The cat, meanwhile, lay like a dead creature, only the rasping, uncertain breathing to show that it was, in fact, alive.

Dave was in a moral dilemma, and he was having a great deal of trouble sorting it out. He knew the cat was legally a noxious animal, a pest that should be destroyed and a danger, if it lived, to the native animals and birds of the region.

But he also knew that he couldn't kill it in cold blood as it slept, regardless of the fact that he *should* and, indeed, regardless of the fact that it was probably best for the cat as well. Because to take it from the bush, assuming he could move it any further without killing it in the process, would mean keeping it in captivity. For any wild animal, that was intrinsically wrong. No full-grown wild creature could be effectively tamed. Made manageable by human standards, perhaps, but not tamed in the sense that it could be happy with its lot. And certainly never a cat, which of all man's pets was the least truly domesticated.

Dave looked down at the cat again, then grinned at the realization that he had been sitting and petting the cat. "And I don't even much *like* cats," he said with a chuckle. He noticed the fire was almost burned out. Rising, he walked further into the copse of underbrush for more dry wood. When he returned a few minutes later, he found that the cat hadn't moved, but Dave fancied its breathing might have become a trifle easier.

It was as he stoked up the dying fire, his eyes and hands busy, that he sensed the change. He turned his head very slowly to find the cat's great luminous eyes fixed upon his own. No hint of gratitude, no friendliness, just the rigid stare of the eyes like blue ice. The cat didn't budge, and the great blue eyes stayed locked on Dave's own. Then a paw twitched, and Dave saw the slow but careful contraction of the cat's lips as it drew them back to reveal its fangs.

"It's all right, old son. I'm not going to hurt you." Dave didn't move any part of his body, but inwardly he shivered with something approaching fear. It was like staring into the eyes of a tiger, eyes that were filled with a wildness no human could really comprehend. He knew, of course, that the cat couldn't hurt him, and that it would be more likely in any event to flee than to try and attack him. But the coldness, the alien hostility in those eyes was fearsome.

The cat shivered and coughed lightly, the cough mingled with a hiss of fear and what might have been almost anger.

"It's all right, it's all right." The words came unbidden, and so softly Dave wasn't even sure he'd spoken. But the cat's eyes flashed brightly for an instant and its lips curled back into a sneer as the hackles rose on its neck. Dave kept his gaze locked on the animal's eyes, careful to move not so much as a finger, and barely allowing himself to breathe.

And then, suddenly, he knew the cat was dying. The realization smashed its way into his mind even as the fog rose, like the finest of morning mist, to cloud over the brightness of the cat's glistening blue eyes.

Leaving the fire, Dave dug a grave deep into the hillside below a large, overhanging rock. The damp soil gave easily, but even so, he was breathing heavily when he finished and his throat was strangely choked with unexpected emotion.

It was all for the best, and he knew it, but he was deeply saddened by the pending death of such a splendid wild creature, even though it should never have been wild in the first place. But better dead than caged, and his memory of the cat's cold, alien eyes had only confirmed that belief.

He searched along the hillside until he found a piece of relatively soft, chalky rock. After stumping back to the grave-site and heaving a large, black boulder next to it, he took the chalky stone and carefully scratched C A T on its flat surface.

Lighting his pipe, he stared at the rising tendrils of smoke as they curled in the sunlight. No use putting it off, he thought.

Resolutely, he turned back to the fire.

The flames had died.

Embers smoldered.

The blanket was empty.